Horizons

Health 2

Healthy and Growing

Teacher's Guide

Organizer / Writer
Gene Ezell

Major Contributors
Judy Cook, Judy Bredeweg, Dennis Vander Plaats,
Anne VanderWoude, Patricia Knoester, Jesslyn DeBoer

Supervising Editor
Hazel Timmer

Executive Editor
Alan Christopherson

Design and Layout
Leann Kruger

Alpha Omega Publications, Inc. • Rock Rapids, IA

2015-2016
1st Quarter L 1-13
2nd Quarter L 14-27
3rd Quarter L 28-41
4th Quarter L 42-54

Horizons Health 2 Teacher's Guide

© MMVII by Alpha Omega Publications, Inc.
804 N. 2nd Ave. E., Rock Rapids, IA 51246-1759
All rights reserved.

CHRISTIAN SCHOOLS INTERNATIONAL

The framework for this curriculum was provided by:
CHRISTIAN SCHOOLS INTERNATIONAL
3350 East Paris Ave. SE
Grand Rapids, Michigan 49512-3054

Printed in the United States of America

ISBN 978-0-7403-1495-7

CONTENTS

31

43

48

54

ACKNOWLEDGMENTS

In the summer of 1989, a new health curriculum for Christian schools was planned. That fall a survey of teachers was conducted in grades K-6. The survey indicated that health was becoming an increasingly significant component of the elementary school curriculum. The survey also revealed that Christian school teachers were eager to have materials containing a clear biblical perspective.

Dr. Gene Ezell, a professor of health education at the University of Tennessee at Chattanooga, developed a content outline and scope and sequence for the *Horizons Health* series. He also was the first author of materials for teacher guides.

Many other individuals helped in the preparation of teacher guides for kindergarten, grade one, and grade two. The materials were reviewed and field tested in several schools during the 1990-91 academic year. Also providing input, critiques, and suggestions were Judy Cook, Judy Bredeweg, Dennis VanderPlaats, Anne VanderWoude, Patricia Knoester, and Jesslyn DeBoer.

The publications program was directed by Gordon L. Bordewyk. The supervising editor for *Horizons Health* was Hazel Timmer. Judy Bandstra oversaw production of the materials, and Cheryl Strikwerda Randall created the illustrations.

"Changing" by Mary Ann Hoberman. Copyright © 1981 by Mary Ann Hoberman. Reprinted by permission of Gina Maccoby Literary Agency. (Unit 1, Lesson 4)

"Up in the Pine" by Nancy Dingman Watson from *Blueberries Lavendar*. Copyright © 1977 by Addison-Wesley Publishing. Used by permission. (Unit 2, Lesson 5)

"Forgive Me, God, For Things I Do" by Elizabeth McE. Shields, st. 1; Sandra Myhr Anderson, st. 2; and Beverly Schultz Mullins, st. 3 from *Prayers for Little Children* by Mary Alice Jones. Copyright © 1949 by Checkerboard Press, Inc. Used by permission. (Unit 2, Lesson 5)

"Jimmy Jet and His TV Set" by Shel Silverstein from *Where the Sidewalk Ends*. Copyright © 1974 by Evil Eye Music, Inc. Reprinted by permission of HarperCollins Publishers. (Unit 5, Lesson 3)

Role of the Christian School in Health Education

The primary responsibility for educating children belongs to parents. But in the Christian community parents do not have that responsibility alone—church and school also participate in the task of education. The church nurtures the faith of its young members, leading them to understand the implications of faith for their lives. The Christian school teaches children and young people about God's world, equipping them for lives of service. Deriving its authority to educate from the parents who send their children to the school, the Christian school supports and augments instruction provided in the home by teaching all curriculum subjects from a biblical perspective.

One curriculum subject is properly health education. Historically this subject has had low priority in curriculum planning; however, among educators today there is a growing awareness of the importance of health education in a balanced curriculum. Educators are recognizing that in order to promote the well-rounded development of children, the school must give sufficient attention to the healthful living of children as individuals and as members of families and communities. A sequential and comprehensive health education curriculum, such as the *Horizons Health* series, provides the Christian school with the opportunity to deal with basic life issues from a Christian perspective in a consistent way.

The serious health problems facing the contemporary world — the threat of AIDS, the widespread use of recreational drugs, the prevalence of teenage pregnancy, the easy access to abortion—underscore the need for a sound, Christian program of health education. More than ever before students need current, accurate information and clear direction on healthful living. Today's health crises dramatically highlight the obligation of home, church, and school to work together to bring the lordship of Christ to bear on the health education of the community's children.

General Christian Perspective

A Christian perspective on health education begins with the Bible's account of who we are and why we are here. The Bible tells us that we have been created by God in his image. We have been created male and female. We have been created to live in harmony with God, with each other, and with the rest of creation. And we have been assigned the task of caring for God's world.

The Bible has more to tell us. It tells us that because of sin our relationship with God is broken; because of sin we no longer clearly reflect God's image. We live at odds with God and with one another. We don't take care of the created world the way God intended. Even when we try our hardest, we often end up doing the evil we don't want to do (Romans 7:19). And physical death is inevitable.

But that's not the end of our story. In Christ, God has broken the cycle of sin and death. In Christ, God is making us whole. In Christ, God is restoring our relationship to him and to one another. In Christ, we are able to experience the beginning of new life—eternal life—and the hope of a new heaven and earth. We look forward to complete renewal and restoration.

It is this story of redemption history that provides the underlying perspective on health education in the Christian school. When we talk about family life, sexuality, physical fitness, death and dying, and other health topics, it is always in the context of this story.

Christian Perspective and Health Education

Christians believe that God created each human being as an organic unity. The Genesis 2 account of creation says that the Lord God formed man from the dust, breathed into him the breath of life, "and the man became a living being" (verse 7). The Bible does refer to various aspects of the person—such as the mind, flesh, soul, spirit, or heart—but the stress is on the unity of the whole being. The various aspects of a person—the intellectual, emotional, social, spiritual, and physical—are interdependent. In the New Testament the apostle Paul, writing to Corinthian Christians, supports this point of view. Some Corinthians, influenced by their pagan culture, apparently believed that gluttony, drunkenness, or promiscuous sexual activity did not affect their "spiritual" life. Paul counters by strongly denouncing this attitude (1 Corinthians 6: 12-19).

What is the significance of this Christian view of the person for education? It means that health education cannot be treated as incidental to the curriculum. Rather, it must be an integral part of the curriculum at every level. Physical fitness, nutrition, personal health, emotional health, the functioning of body systems—all strands of the health curriculum—affect the whole child. We must recognize that since healthy living affects us in our totality, health education plays a solid role in developing children and equipping them to serve God in the world.

• •

God has given human beings the task of caring for creation. This task includes being caretakers of ourselves. The *Horizons Health* series helps students fulfill their God-given responsibility in several ways. It teaches them about proper personal and dietary health and encourages them to make good choices in these areas. For example, students learn about the different nutritional value in various foods, how family backgrounds and lifestyles influence eating patterns, and the importance of cleanliness in handling and consuming foods. The series also teaches students about personal safety, helping them to handle emergencies and to take precautions to avoid injury and harm. Another strand of *Horizons Health* deals with body systems, and students come to understand how they are "fearfully and wonderfully made." Still another strand deals with disease. In this area students learn, for example, about the defenses which God has provided for our bodies, and how each person can help prevent the spread of disease. The strand of emotional and mental health leads students to develop an honest and healthy self-image concept and to deal with feelings in wholesome ways. Finally, a curriculum strand dealing with substance use and abuse acquaints students with the risks associated with tobacco, alcohol, and drugs.

The Christian view of a person's responsibility to care for himself or herself in order to honor God runs counter to the prevailing view in North American culture. Our culture says that what we do with our body is an individual matter. Sports and fitness are often used for self-glorification, elevating the body to a higher status than it warrants. At the same time, abuse of the body through addiction, inattention to nutrition, or lack of exercise is also common. In a culture such as this, spelling out how we honor God with healthful living and nurturing Christian attitudes toward ourselves and others are crucial for the Christian community.

• •

The Christian's view of death and dying also differs from the view prevalent in society. Christians recognize disease and death as part of sin's effects on creation. Physical death is inevitable, but for those who have new life in Christ, death is not the last word. However, even though Christ has removed death's ultimate sting, death is still the Christian's enemy (1 Corinthians 15: 26, 55).

One strand of the *Horizons Health* series helps students view death and dying from this Christian perspective. In ways appropriate to the developmental levels of the students, the curriculum deals honestly with topics such as fear of death, inevitability of death, and ways Christians cope with death and dying.

• •

Christians are called to reflect God's love in all their relationships. The social health strand of the health curriculum assists students to develop mature Christian attitudes towards others. They also learn interpersonal skills necessary for getting along with others. Thus students are lead to become contributing members of their communities. To answer our deepest needs, God created us to live in relationship with others.

Christians believe that marriage and family are part of a loving God's design for the human race. God, reflecting on his creation, decided that it was not good for Adam to be alone: "I will make a suitable helper for him" (Genesis 2:18). So God established marriage — and by extension, the family — as a cornerstone of creation. As part of God's creation, marriage was very good. The Bible has such a high view of marriage that it uses marriage as a symbol of the relationship of Christ and the Church.

But marriage and family have not escaped the effects of sin. Sin's results are loneliness, alienation, the breaking of family relationships, and the collapse of marriages. In North American society, these effects of sin are also clearly evident. In fact, for some, marriage and the family simply seem outdated institutions that are no longer useful. And pursuing a course of self-fulfillment is held up by many as the highest goal of life.

Christians believe that in Jesus Christ there is healing for brokenness and power to restore family relationships. He calls us to a life of service and responsibility in the family. And although our efforts are imperfect and our homes are not free of trouble, by God's grace family life can be a source of comfort and joy.

The family life strand of the *Horizons Health* series leads students to appreciate the blessings of family life and to assume responsibilities of family membership. Working through family topics—such as resolving conflicts, the importance of basing family life on God's law, knowing how sexuality affects life, and caring for sexuality in a way pleasing to God—helps students to establish basic Christian life patterns, patterns that will have a far-reaching effect on their lives.

• •

In summary, the *Horizons Health* curriculum seeks to teach Christian students how the lordship of Christ results in healthful living. For only as students acknowledge their accountability to God and form their lives according to his Word are they able to become all their Creator wants them to become and live lives of thankfulness and service.

OVERVIEW

1. What is Horizons Health?

Horizons Health is a comprehensive health education curriculum for grades K-8. The series addresses the mental, emotional, social, and spiritual aspects of health as well as the physical. It helps students take responsibility for their health as individuals and as members of families and communities. It gives them opportunity to develop basic life skills — such as communicating, decision making, and resolving conflicts — in order to prepare them to meet the challenges of daily living. Its Christian perspective leads students to recognize that a healthy lifestyle is a lifestyle of obedience to God.

2. How is the curriculum organized?

Horizons Health is a flexible curriculum, organized into independent units. The units can be taught in any order, depending on your curriculum needs. Each unit focuses primarily on one or two main strands of the curriculum, with lesser strands integrated where appropriate. These are the eleven strands, which are addressed at each grade level:

Emotional/Mental Health
Social Health/Interpersonal Skills
Family Life/Human Sexuality
Growth and Development
Personal Health
Community Health

Nutrition
Disease Prevention
Safety and First Aid
Substance Use and Abuse
Consumer Health

The scope and sequence chart shows the topics covered in each strand at this grade level and at the other grade levels of the series.

3. Do concepts covered in health education overlap with those covered in other content areas?

Because this is a comprehensive health program rather than a single-topic program, overlap unavoidably occurs in certain content areas. Health education, for example, teaches students about how their bodies work and how substance use and abuse, physical fitness, and nutrition can effect body structures and functions; however, structure and function of body systems may currently be taught in science. Schools may wish to integrate areas that overlap.

4. What is the personal safety component of Horizons Health?

At grades K-2 the safety unit includes a lesson on stranger education. In addition, at each level from kindergarten through grade 8 there is one lesson in the safety unit on preventing sexual abuse. In age-appropriate ways, each level deals with differentiating appropriate and inappropriate touch, developing self-protection skills, and identifying sources of help in case of abuse.

Since personal safety is a sensitive area, schools should inform parents about the content of these lessons. Clear communication not only creates trust within the community but also ensures that parents will support and reinforce personal safety concepts taught at school.

Before teaching lessons on personal safety, schools should also develop and adopt a protocol for dealing with suspected or reported abuse. Contact the provincial or state department responsible for child protective services to obtain information and copies of relevant laws. Schools interested in obtaining samples of school policy statements on child welfare that include a protocol for dealing with abuse should contact organizations like the Ontario Alliance of Christian Schools, 617 Garner Road East, Ancaster, Ontario L9G 3K9; or the Society of Christian Schools in British Columbia, 7600 Glover Road, Langley, British Columbia V2Y 1Y1.

5. What is the sex education component of Horizons Health?

Sex education is placed within the broader context of family life and human sexuality, one of the strands of the curriculum. Thus at every level *Horizons Health* deals with concepts relating to human sexuality. The grade 5 unit "Growing and Changing" deals specifically with the onset of puberty and the changes it brings.

6. Is AIDS education included in the health program?

AIDS education is integrated into the program as part of the disease prevention strand. At levels K-2 there are no AIDS-specific lessons; however, the broader health issues and concepts addressed at these levels—preventing communicable disease, the relationship between personal choices and health, and our God-given responsibility to honor and care for our body—establish the foundation for understanding AIDS-specific concepts at higher grades. At levels 3-6 students learn about AIDS and HIV in age-appropriate ways. Grade 5 material has a lesson on sexually transmitted diseases, including AIDS/HIV.

7. How can schools best implement a comprehensive health education?

Planning a strategy to implement the program is crucial for the curriculum to be effective. Three main areas to address are these: keeping parents informed and involved, assisting teachers with resources and training in specialized areas, and providing a school environment that supports the program.

First, parents need to be informed and involved. Because some topics covered in health are controversial, good communication is particularly important. Meeting with parents at the beginning of the year to discuss the content and goals of health education and sending letters home to inform parents about what students are learning and doing in *Horizons Health* (particularly in advance of lessons dealing with sensitive issues) are good basic strategies. Involving parents strengthens the program as health concepts learned at school are reinforced at home.

Second, schools need to provide teachers with resources and training. Many health education curricula have compulsory teacher-training sessions because of the special challenges a comprehensive health education program presents. Some health topics have traditionally not been part of the school curriculum in a formal way, and few teachers have had courses in health education. Thus teachers need opportunities through workshops or in-service training to become comfortable in dealing with sensitive areas such as sexual abuse and substance abuse. In addition, they need resources to support the curriculum and to keep current on health issues. Local or provincial/state agencies and volunteer agencies (for example, the American/Canadian Red Cross or American/Canadian Lung Association) are sources of valuable assistance and offer a wealth of resources. In some cases, inviting experts into the classroom may be advisable.

Third, the total school environment should support the health curriculum and reinforce classroom lessons. Students learn in the classroom about eating snacks that are nutritious and "tooth smart," but does the school ask students to take part in an annual candy sale to raise money for the school? Does the school library contain current materials about a wide variety of wellness issues? What does the climate of the school teach about interpersonal relationships, about living in community? Does the school community model what a Christian community should be? Health education cannot end when students step out of the classroom. Schools need to consider what kind of messages the total environment is sending.

USING HORIZONS HEALTH

The curriculum consists of independent units that can be taught in any order. This flexible design makes it possible for you to choose segments that meet your curriculum needs and your time schedule. The unit summaries found at the beginning of each unit give a quick overview of the unit and help you decide which units or lessons to use.

There are approximately 50 lessons at each of the K-2 levels. With a time schedule of a 30- to 40-minute session for each lesson, *Horizons Health* requires daily sessions for 12 to 14 weeks (or 17-19 weeks teaching three sessions per week and 25-27 weeks teaching two sessions per week). An interdisciplinary program, health lends itself to integration with other subjects, such as Bible, language arts, music, art, science, and social studies. Suggestions for integration are included throughout the curriculum.

Horizons Health provides a carefully planned and comprehensive framework for teaching health education. It is meant to furnish guidelines and suggestions; it is not meant to prescribe each step of each lesson. You are the one to mold and adapt the material and translate it to fit your students and your community.

Format, K-2

The units begin with an overview that includes the following components:

- A *Unit Summary* gives an "at-a-glance" list of lessons.
- *Goals* for the unit are outlined.
- The *Background* provides Christian perspective and/or helpful unit information.
- *Vocabulary* lists words students need to know to understand unit health concepts.
- *Unit Resources* offers suggestions of titles of organizations, books, kits, or audiovisuals helpful as teacher or student resources to support the unit as a whole.
- *Lesson Resources* suggests materials for specific lessons. Most of these resources are listed again in the lesson.

The lessons follow this format:
- *Preparation/Materials* lists what things are needed for the lesson and describes necessary preparations.
- *Objectives* for the lesson are outlined.
- *Background* appears in selected lessons providing specific information on health issues, alerting teachers to sensitive lesson topics, or providing Christian perspective.
- The *Lesson* offers a step-by-step outline. Each lesson ends with a suggestion for closing, providing an opportunity for reflection, self-awareness, summary, or evaluation.
- *Related Activities* presents additional suggestions for student activities, expanding or extending the lesson.

Masters for Teacher Visuals are located in the back of the Teacher Guide.

Resources

Multimedia resources can significantly increase the impact of the health curriculum, and numerous suggestions for resources have been included. Few health education resources, however, are written from a Christian perspective. Careful screening is necessary before using resources in the classroom. In some cases, you may decide to use selected sections or perhaps to use the materials but add a critical evaluation.

The listings provide suggestions for current resources, but keep in mind that the health field changes rapidly. So although we have included resources that are current at the time of publication, you will need to re-examine and refurbish resources to keep the curriculum up-to-date.

Many community and national volunteer health organizations offer educational materials in their special areas. These materials, which include kits, songs, filmstrips, audiocassettes, lesson plans, activities, posters, student booklets, or brochures for parents, are often available at minimal cost. Many of the materials produced by these organizations are listed in the Unit or Lesson Resources. A list of national health organizations is included at the end of the Introduction. Because new materials are constantly being produced, contacting these health organizations periodically will help you to tap an ongoing source of valuable resources.

Music

Singing together is an activity that builds community. All take part; all share in creating a delightful whole. Singing encourages togetherness, and young children usually enjoy singing and love repeating favorite songs. At the K and 1 levels particularly, *Horizons Health* includes many suggestions for piggyback songs. In addition, a few songs are included in curriculum.

Singing to God is also a natural part of curriculum in the Christian school. God's people of all ages join voices in praise and thanks to God. At the K-2 levels of *Horizons Health*, we have suggested songs that fit with some of the lessons or units. The suggestions are from the following songbooks. If you wish to obtain copies of the books, order them from your local music supplier or directly from the publisher.

Children's Hymnbook. Grand Rapids: Christian Schools International and Eerdmans, 1962.
> Order from Christian Schools International, 3350 East Paris Ave. S.E., Grand Rapids, Michigan 49512; phone 800-635-8288.

Proclaim Songbook 1 and 2. Minneapolis: Augsburg, 1981.
   Order from Augsburg Publishing Co., 426 Fifth St., Box 1209, Minneapolis, Minnesota 19103; phone 800-328-4648.

Psalter Hymnal. Grand Rapids: Christian Reformed Board of Publications, 1986.
   Order from CRC Publications, 2850 Kalamazoo Ave., Grand Rapids, Michigan 49560; phone 800-333-8300.

Songs of God's Love: A Hymnal for Primary Children. St. Louis: Concordia, 1984.
   Order from Concordia Publishing House, 3558 S. Jefferson Ave., St. Louis, Missouri 63118; phone 314-664-7000.

Songs to Grow on. Kansas City, Mo.: Lillenas, 1980.
   Order from Lillenas Publishing Co., P.O. Box 527, Kansas City, Missouri 64141; phone 816-931-1900.

HEALTH EDUCATION RESOURCES

American Alliance for Health, Physical Education, Recreation, and Dance (AAHPERD)
1900 Association Drive
Reston, Virginia 22091
800-321-0789; 703-476-3481

Canadian Association for Health, Physical Education, Recreation, and Dance (CAHPERD)
Place R. Tait McKenzie
1600 James Naismith Drive
Gloucester, Ontario K1B 5N4
613-748-5622
    AAHPERD and CAHPERD are national organizations committed to promoting
    health and fitness through a wide variety of programs and publications.

National Clearinghouse for Alcohol and Drug Information
P.O. Box 2345
Rockville, Maryland 20847
800-729-6686
http://ncadi.samhsa.gov

National Family Partnership
2490 Coral way, Suite 501
Miami, FL 33145
800-705-8997

Office of Disease Prevention and Health Promotion (ODPHP) National Health Information Center
P.O. Box 1133
Washington, D.C. 20012-1133
800-336-4797 or 301-565-4167
    Publishes Healthfinder, which lists health education materials (primarily for grades
    K-6) produced by national and professional organizations. ODPHP provides
    ordering addresses and prices, but does not evaluate the materials or sources.

Parents Against Drugs (PAD)
70 Maxome Avenue
Willowdale, Ontario M2M 3K1
416-225-6604
    Offers current information about drug abuse and a drug awareness workshop for
    educators.

PRIDE Canada

Suite 111, Thorvaldson Building

College of Pharmacy, University of Saskatchewan

Saskatoon, Saskatchewan S7N 0W0

800-667-3747

PRIDE, Inc. - United States

100 Edgewood Avenue, Suite 1002

Atlanta, Georgia 30303

800-241-7946

Parents' Resource Institute for Drug Education (PRIDE) both in Canada and in United States and Canada provides drug education resources, training sessions, and toll-free hot lines.

U.S. Department of Health and Human Services

Public Health Service

Centers for Disease Control

Center for Chronic Disease Prevention and Health Promotion

Division of Adolescent and School Health

Atlanta, Georgia 30333

404-488-5372

Offers resource suggestions and updated information about AIDS/HIV. Listed materials include audiovisuals, books and book chapters, brochures, teaching guides and curricula, instructional packages, scripts, and comic books.

SCOPE AND SEQUENCE

	Growth and Development	Disease Prevention	Substance Use/Abuse
K	• growth awareness • five senses and corresponding body parts • primary/secondary teeth	• germs and disease • preventing spread of germs • effect of smoke on lungs	• defining medicine • rule: only adults give medicine • consulting adult before using any unknown substance • choosing a smoke-free environment
1	• review of five senses • naming external body parts • joints • four main organs: brain, heart, stomach, lungs • interrelationship of body parts • growth predictions • primary/secondary teeth	• defining communicable/noncommunicable disease • preventing spread of germs • immunizations • health checkups • effect of smoking on lungs	• differentiating drugs and medicines • symbols for hazardous substances • identifying some drugs
2	• growth awareness • introduction to body systems • function and interdependence of senses • function and basic structure of eyes and ears • visual/hearing impairments	• disease symptoms • defining bacteria and viruses • how germs enter body • effects of nicotine, alcohol, and caffeine on body • identifying eye problems	• identifying common drugs: alcohol, tobacco, and caffeine • products containing caffeine • effect of caffeine on body • how nicotine enters the body • how alcohol affects physical reactions • differentiating prescription and over-the-counter drugs • reasons for using medicine
3	• overview of body systems: skin, muscular, skeletal, digestive, respiratory, circulatory, nervous, excretory (main parts and interrelationships) • growth and development problems (special populations)	• communicable and chronic diseases • AIDS transmission through blood and hypodermic needles • immunizations, proper food storage, and cleanliness as ways to control disease	• defining terms • proper use vs. misuse of substances • influence of advertising on use of over-the-counter medicines • dosages • labels for information • tolerance and addiction • harmful effects of tobacco, smoking
4	• miracle of life • hereditary factors • structure and function of blood • the immune system • hair, skin, and nails • structure and function of teeth • digestive system: parts of, process of digestion • cells/tissues/organs/systems • functions and kinds of cells	• care of skin • diseases of digestive system • lack of nutrients and disease • alcoholism • long term/short term effects of smoking • review HIV transmission through blood, needles	• review of terms: drugs, medicines, substance, prescription, OTC • side effects of medications • avoiding misuse of OTCs • harmful effects of tobacco, alcohol, marijuana, cocaine • defining alcoholism • refusal skills
5	• respiratory system • variations in growth rates • endocrine system • physical, emotional, and social changes of puberty • reproductive system	• main classes of pathogens • chain of infection • some common communicable diseases • preventing respiratory diseases • sexually transmitted diseases, including characteristics, transmission, and prevention of HIV infection	• review of terminology • demonstrating effect of smoking on lungs • refusal skills
6	• fetal development • stages of life • processes by which cells receive nutrients and oxygen: diffusion, filtration, osmosis • review of main body systems, main parts and functions • hereditary and environmental factors • impairments	• preventing cardiovascular disease • risk factors of cardiovascular disease • diseases of muscular, skeletal, and nervous systems • hereditary and environmental factors in disease • alcoholism and cirrhosis • anorexia and bulimia • AIDS/HIV	• chemical dependency and its effects • steroids • results of substance use • societal pressure to use substances • resisting alcohol advertising • strategies for resisting pressure
7/8	• characteristics of stages of life • review of interdependence of body systems • changes of puberty • review of reproductive system • impairments • identifying learning styles	• biblical view of disease • lifestyle choices and disease • eating disorders • suntanning • sexually transmitted diseases, including HIV/AIDS • review reducing risk of communicable and acquired diseases • understanding reality of health problems	• alcohol, tobacco, drug abuse (student research) • decision-making and refusal skills

	Nutrition	Emotional/Mental Health	Social Health/Interpersonal Skills
K	• food for energy and growing • plant and animal food sources • eating a variety of foods	• created unique • differences and similarities • main feelings • situations and feelings • responding to others' feelings	• minding manners • manners and feelings • listening to each other • ways to share • cooperating
1	• food and body energy • five food groups • eating from all food groups • eating healthy snacks • diet and tooth health	• created unique • alike and different • naming and exploring feelings • body language • dealing with feelings • ways to deal with anger • developing empathy	• purpose of good manners • practicing good manners • active listening steps • sharing • practicing cooperation
2	• five food groups • limiting extras • daily serving requirements • balanced eating • cleanliness and food handling • eating breakfast • smart snacks for teeth	• identifying individual gifts/interests • blessing others with our gifts • review of main feelings • identifying a variety of feelings • feelings and actions • communicating feelings • developing empathy • saying no and feelings	• communicating with others • developing social skills/manners • showing appreciation • helping others • active listening • selfish/unselfish attitudes • importance of cooperating
3	• classifying foods • combination foods • define nutrients needed for growth, maintenance, repair of body • limited nutritional value of some foods • healthy snacks • diet and tooth decay	• self-awareness and acceptance • appreciating diversity • identifying and expressing feelings • emotions and body feelings • how feelings affect thoughts and actions • dealing with specific emotions: fear, hurt, anger, being left out • humor and feelings	• developing friendships • factors that affect friendships • kinds of friendships • showing kindness toward others • laughing with, not at • active listening • resolving conflicts
4	• six major classes of nutrients: fats, carbohydrates, water, minerals, vitamins, protein • function of nutrients • serving size • lack of nutrients and disease • good food, good times	• self-knowledge and knowledge of God • being saints and sinners • individual differences as part of God's plan • using gifts to serve • how others affect self-concept • showing appreciation for others • handling and expressing feelings • avoiding self-putdowns • making decisions	• belonging to groups other than family • showing respect for others • accepting differences • communication skills • working out problems in interpersonal relationships
5	• review of main nutrients and their sources • vitamins, minerals, and their functions • function of water • individual nutrition requirements • nutrition deficiencies and health • influences on eating patterns	• growing up • identifying individual strengths • range of feelings • developing feelings vocabulary • ways of dealing with emotions • expressing feelings without blaming • overall wellness and emotions • dealing with anger in healthy ways	• wise ways in relationships (Proverbs) • forgiveness and maintaining friendships • respecting others • resolving conflicts • social skills • cooperative skills
6	• criteria for proper food selection • diet analysis • nutrients: carbohydrates, proteins, fats • reducing salt and sugar • results of unbalanced diet • eating disorders	• new life in Christ • patterns of life: inherited and acquired characteristics • handling ups and downs of feelings • interaction of feelings, thoughts, and actions • identifying and managing stress • recognizing influences • decision making and peer influence	• identifying social support network • factors that build up or break down relationships • erecting barriers: prejudice, discrimination, labeling • communication: basic elements, verbal/nonverbal, active listening • deciding to care about others
7/8	• proper nutrition and dieting	• identifying self as God's image bearer and God's child • being made new in Christ • self-talk and self-confidence • discovering, accepting, and developing gifts • using gifts to serve God/community • influence of media on self-concept • decision-making values/strategies • setting goals • developing study skills • being assertive • recognizing and expressing feelings	• biblical view of community • types of love • living in community • dealing with internal/peer pressure • using peer pressure positively • friendship • dealing with conflict • communication

	Family Life/Human Sexuality	Personal Health	Community Health
K	• families—part of God's plan • similarities/differences among families • gender differences • feelings and family • our families and God's family • dealing with death	• good health choices • dressing to stay healthy • exercise and rest • cleanliness and health • care of teeth: brushing and checkups	• health helpers • smoke in environment
1	• living things reproduce • families—part of God's plan • kinds of families • contributing to family life • family changes • death and Christian hope • Christian families in context of God's family	• making healthy choices • staying fit • eating from all food groups • tooth care: plaque, brushing, checkups, diet • grooming and health	• defining pollution • causes of air pollution • health helpers • immunizations
2	• families provide basic needs • human sexuality, a gift of God • exploring gender differences/similarities • resolving conflicts • family rules • new beginnings and forgiveness • family heritage and traditions • dealing with death	• good health habits • keeping fit and active • avoiding too much TV • getting enough sleep • eating a balanced diet • eating healthy snacks and breakfast • review of good grooming habits • tooth care: brushing, flossing, snacks	• noise pollution
3	• God's law of love as the basis of family living • depending on family members • communicating in families • living patterns and culture • life cycle and the family • sexual identity, an integral part of a person • dealing with death	• benefits of fitness • being physically fit; flexibility, endurance, strength • good posture • oral hygiene • eating healthy foods • benefits of sleep	• health agencies • role of community workers in safety
4	• institution of marriage/family • responsibility and family life • family and the wider community • communicating • death and dying	• components of personal health • building physical fitness • importance of cleanliness • posture • sleep and rest	• effect of contaminated food, water, air
5	• wellness in family relationships • family's impact on members' development • foundation of marriage • changes during puberty • authority/freedom in family life • coping with change in family life • death and dying	• concept of wellness • review of personal health practices • keeping a healthy balance • inventory of health habits • fitness and overall health • exercise and respiratory endurance	• air pollution • water pollution and health • community health resources
6	• stages of life/development • courtship, marriage intimacy • beginning of human life • fetal development and birth process • being a Christian family • societal pressures and family life • changes in adolescence and family life • death/dying	• healthy lifestyle • benefits/components of fitness • weight, strength, posture, obesity, losing healthfully • care of skin, eyes, and ears • importance of sleep/rest • oral hygiene • personal cleanliness/disease prevention • setting health goals	• community problems caused by substance abuse • treatment for alcoholism • community health resources
7/8	• family life • sexuality vs. sex • biblical view of sexuality • myths of sex and sexuality • changes in puberty • chastity and abstinence • healthy male-female relationships • sexual abuse	• healthy lifestyle choices • influence of fashion on ideas of beauty • dieting and health • physical fitness and overall wellness • review components of health fitness • review personal hygiene concepts	• community resources for getting help for substance abuse/other health problems

	Consumer Health	Safety/First Aid
K		• rules and safety • poison safety • medicine and safety • traffic safety • strangers and safety • fire safety: basic rules • emergency phoning • appropriate/inappropriate touch
1	• health checkups	• medicine safety • poison safety: basic rules and household poisons • safety and strangers • review of fire safety • car passenger safety • dealing with emergencies • appropriate/inappropriate touch
2	• aid for visual and hearing impaired	• care of eyes and ears • review of stranger education • intro. to bike safety • review of fire safety • home escape plan • seatbelts • emergency phoning • preventing sexual abuse: appropriate/inappropriate/confusing touch • good and bad secrets
3	• influence of ads on use of substances • labels as a source of information • reasons for using common health products	• risk-taking • bicycle safety • water safety • electrical appliances • preventing sexual abuse: appropriate/inappropriate touch, trickery, self-protection, sources of help • action plan for an emergency • first aid: scrapes, nosebleeds, burns, blisters
4		• accidents—emotional, decisional factors • review of basic safety rules • playground safety • bicycle safety • fire safety, flame hazards • home alone • preventing sexual abuse: definition, touch continuum, self-protection
5	• advertising and food choices	• taking responsibility for safety of self and others • basic emergency first aid • rescue breathing • preventing sexual abuse: defining sexual abuse, saying no assertively, sources of help
6	• getting correct health care	• taking responsibility for safety of self and others • safety in extreme hot or cold weather • safety and natural disasters • review of basic safety rules • home hazard check • defining/preventing sexual abuse: • self-protection, sources of help
7/8	• evaluating advertisements • media sales techniques	• review of basic safety and first aid • responding in emergencies • preventing sexual abuse • identifying and practicing self-protection skills

Finding Out About Myself and Others

Goals

- Students will develop a healthy self-awareness.
- Students will develop respect for others' uniqueness and feelings.
- Students will develop their understanding of the role of feelings.
- Students will choose to express feelings in a healthy and responsible way.

Background

Emotional and mental health is the focus of this unit. In it students examine the topic of feelings and recognize more clearly what prompts certain feelings. They learn about handling and expressing their emotions in healthy ways and how to respond in healthy ways to the emotions of others.

What are healthy ways for Christians to deal with emotions? Mary Vander Goot in her book *Healthy Emotions: Helping Children Grow* cautions against two extremes. On one extreme are Christians who promote the idea that good children will have only "nice" feelings. Much popular Christian literature and art promote this idea by picturing only smiling, sweet children. Vander Goot warns that "if we fall into the habit of thinking that pleasant emotions are good and unpleasant emotions are bad, and if we consequently elect to cover up negative emotions rather than attend to them, learn from them, and grow from them, we lose integrity and become emotionally artificial." Showing sadness, fear, or anger is not un-Christian. However, in reaction to this "saccharine" approach, some Christians have gone to the opposite extreme, maintaining that children should have the freedom to express whatever they feel. This approach is dangerously irresponsible. For although disturbing emotions should not be stifled or denied, randomly expressing emotions with no concern for others or failing to deal with their causes is also not healthy.

To deal with emotions in a healthy way we must recognize and express the rich variety of human emotions. But we must also learn to control our emotions, to act on them responsibly. Vander Goot puts it this way: "Although our emotions are woven in with our actions, they are counselors to our actions but not their dictators. Our emotions give us a strong sense of our condition; however, we must make insightful and responsible decisions when we act to alter our condition."

To stay emotionally healthy takes maintenance. Vander Goot singles out three goals to work toward: richness, fit, and control. The first goal, richness, means being able to express a wide variety of feelings. Many people live impoverished emotional lives. Although there are many reasons for this, sometimes family and societal patterns are the cause. Some families, for example, don't allow open expressions of appreciation, affection, or fear; society frowns upon men expressing fear or sadness and upon women expressing anger. A narrow emotional life has wide implications because it keeps us from understanding the emotions of others and thus affects our relationships with others. Fit, the second goal, has to do with how emotions connect with events. Emotions must be fitting; they need to be appropriate to an event. "A pleasant feeling in the face of a horrid event is false, and despair in the presence of great possibilities is equally false," comments Vander Goot. We have a choice as to how to express our feelings. The goal is to work toward fitting emotions and fitting expressions of emotion. Control, the third goal, requires a purpose in life, something to give our lives direction. Only in the light of that purpose or commitment are we able to assess our emotional life and work toward reflecting that commitment in our emotions. The goal of control is not to stifle emotions, but to follow up on emotions "wisely so that our feelings, our relationships, our actions, and our perceptions move toward greater and greater integrity."

Christ, whose kingly rule includes our emotional life, calls us to be his disciples, to live according to the laws of the kingdom of God. By God's grace we can learn to become aware of the meaning of our feelings and to act on them in ways that lead us and our neighbors to emotional health.

Vocabulary

Integrate the following suggested vocabulary:

unique	feelings	healthy	lonely	ashamed
create	right	emotions	jealous	disappointed
angry	wrong	joyful	worried	bless/blessing
sad	situation	calm	silly	body language
happy	dangerous	confused	excited	mean
afraid	surprised	loving	frustrated	embarrassed

Unit Resources

All Together: Our Multicultural Community. Kit. National Film Board of Canada, 1984.
> This kit, which includes two filmstrips, audiocassettes (*All My Colours* and *All My Friends*) and a teacher guide, aims to develop tolerance and acceptance of differences both cultural and individual.

Borba, Michele and Craig. *Self-Esteem: A Classroom Affair.* Volumes 1 and 2. San Francisco: Harper, 1984 and 1985.
> Contains ideas for activities and reproducible worksheets.

Canfield, Jack, and Harold C. Wells. *100 Ways to Enhance Self-Concept in the Classroom: A Handbook for Teachers and Parents.* Englewood Cliffs, N. J.: Prentice-Hall, 1976.
> This classic contains suggestions for building an environment of positive support, increasing student self-awareness, and improving relationships with others.

Joosse, Wayne. *The Christian's Self-Image: Issues and Implications.* Occasional Papers from Calvin College. Grand Rapids: Calvin College, 1989.
> A critical look at the self-esteem movement.

Meagher, Laura. *Teaching Children About Global Awareness.* Lexington, N.Y.: Crossroad, 1991.
> Meagher offers valuable suggestions for promoting global awareness in children.

Prelutsky, Jack, compiler. *The Random House Book of Poetry for Children.* New York: Random House, 1983.
> A good source of poetry that honestly expresses children's feelings. Some suggestions: "Wrestling" by Kathleen Fraser, "Keziah" by Gwendolyn Brooks, "When I Was Lost," by

Dorothy Aldis, "Sulk" and They're Calling" by Felice Holman.

The Pine Tree Club. Videocassette. Grand Rapids: Pine Rest Life Enrichment Center, 1988.
Intended for grades K-4, this 36-minute video teaches these rules of positive behavior: everyone is equal; it's o.k. to be different; respect others; say "no" when something is wrong; express feelings in a responsible way. To order, contact the Pine Rest Life Enrichment Center, 300 68th St. S.E., Grand Rapids, Michigan 49508.

Prutzman, Priscilla, and others. *The Friendly Classroom for a Small Planet.* Philadelphia: New Society Publishers, 1988.
This resource is put out by Children's Creative Response to Conflict, an organization with Quaker roots. It contains suggestions/activities for building community, learning to communicate, promoting self-awareness and empathy. Order from the publisher: P.O. Box 582, Santa Cruz, California 95061.

Sofield, Juliano and Hammett. *Design for Wholeness: Dealing With Anger, Learning to Forgive, Building Self-Esteem.* Notre Dame, Ind.: Ave Maria Press, 1990.
Written from Christian (Roman Catholic) perspective, this resource contains helpful background material for teachers.

Vander Goot, Mary. *Healthy Emotions: Helping Children Grow.* Grand Rapids: Baker, 1987.
Written from a solid Christian perspective, this resource is "about normal emotions of normal children." The author's purpose is to help adults deal effectively with children's emotions. In chapter 7, "Teachers and School," Vander Goot reflects on the way the school environment influences the emotional development of children.

You, Me, and Others—Variety. White Plains, NY: March of Dimes, 1985.
This resource, which is part of the March of Dimes' curriculum on genetics, has five lessons that explore variations among individuals: (1) "Is It Alive? (2) "We Are Alike & Different," (3) "How Tall?" (4) "What Do I Like?" (5) "My Body." Suggested learning activities are listed for each grade level, and 5 activity masters are included. Contact the local chapter of March of Dimes to obtain the materials.

Lesson Resources
Lesson 1
Ideas, Thoughts, and Feelings. Audiocassette. Educational Activities.
"I Like Me" and "I Don't Like Me" are two songs that tie in with the lesson.

Lungs Are for Life - 2. Kit. American Lung Association, 1983.
This kit includes a teacher guide, activity sheets, and two posters (one entitled: "Taking Off: Looking at Our Feelings"). Although the focus of the material is healthy lungs, the main concept of the opening unit, Getting to Know You, is self-awareness. Contact the local chapter of the American Lung Association to find out how to obtain the kit.

Sharmat, Marjorie. *Helga High-Up.* New York: Scholastic, 1987.
Helga the giraffe learns to appreciate herself.

Stouse, Karla F. *Different Is Kind of Nice.* St. Meinrad, Ind.: Abbey, 1987.
For grades 2 and up.

Spier, Peter. *People.* New York: Doubleday, 1980.
    Detailed illustrations picture the wide diversity of people.

Lesson 2

Aliki. *Feelings.* New York: Greenwillow, 1984.

Berger, Terry. *I Have Feelings.* Human Science Press, 1971.
    A 40-page book exploring 17 different feelings and situations that evoke each. Photographs help children identify the feelings.

Cohen, Miriam. *Jim's Dog Muffins.* New York: Greenwillow, 1984.
    Jim feels sad when his pet Muffins dies.

Fernandes, Eugenie. *A Difficult Day.* Toronto: Kids Can Press, 1987.
    Melinda is feeling grouchy until her mother's freshly-baked cookies turn things around.

Fiday, Beverly and David. *Time to Go.* New York: Harcourt, 1990.
    A child sadly says goodbye to the family farm.

Kachenmeister, Cherryl. *On Monday When It Rained.* Boston: Houghton, 1989.
    A boy tells about what happened each day of the week, and photographs show how he felt each day.

Krasilovsky, Phyllis. *The Shy Little Girl.* Topeka, Kansas.
    Anne and Claudia who are both shy, become friends. It gradually becomes easier for them to join in with their classmates.

Moss, Marissa. *Regina's Big Mistake.* Boston: Houghton, 1990.
    Regina's feelings about a drawing assignment that goes wrong will be familiar to all children.

Murphy, Elspeth. *Sometimes I Have to Cry: Verses from the Psalms on Tears.* Weston, Ont./Elgin, Ill.: Cook, 1988.

_____. *Sometimes I Think "What If?" Psalm 46 for Children.* Weston, Ont./Elgin, Ill.: Cook, 1987.
    A child imagines a series of disasters but finds peace knowing that God is in charge and "right here."

Simon, Norma. *I Am Not a Cry Baby.* Niles, Ill.: Whitman, 1989.
    It's all right to cry because often there are good reasons for crying.

Tester, Sylvia. *Moods and Emotions.* Marvel Education.
    A set of 16 dramatic pictures portraying emotions such as love, joy, anger, fear, sorrow, satisfaction, frustration and protectiveness. Accompanied by a 40-page manual of suggestions for classroom use.

Viorst, Judith. *Alexander and the Terrible, Horrible, No Good, Very Bad Day.* New York: Macmillian, 1972.

Williams, Marcia. *Not a Worry in the World.* New York: Crown, 1990.
    A lighthearted book that helps children laugh at some common worries.

Lessons 3 and 4

Aliki. *We Are Best Friends.* New York: Greenwillow, 1982.

Borgeois, Paulette. *Franklin in the Dark.* Toronto: Kids Can Press, 1986.

_____. *Franklin Fibs.* Toronto: Kids Can Press, 1991.

Cohen, Miriam. *Jim Meets the Thing.* New York: Greenwillow, 1981.

DeJong, Meindert. *Nobody Plays With a Cabbage.* New York: Harper, 1962.

Greenfield, Eloise. *She Come Bringing Me That Little Baby Girl.* New York: Harper, 1990.

Grimes, Nikki. *Something on My Mind.* New York: Dutton, 1978.

Hayes, Sarah. *Mary, Mary.* New York: McElderry, 1990.
    A little girl responds to a giant's loneliness.

Keats, Ezra Jack. *The Trip.* New York: Morrow, 1987.

Marshall, James. *What's the Matter With Carruthers?* Boston: Houghton, 1972.

Munsch, Robert. *Mortimer.* Willowdale, Ont.: Annick Press, 1983.

Murphy, Elspeth. *God Cares When I'm Feeling Mean.* Weston, Ont./Elgin, Ill.: Cook, 1985.

Schindler, Regine. *A Miracle for Sarah.* Nashville: Abingdon, 1985.

Sharmat, Marjorie. *Bartholomew the Bossy.* New York: Macmillan, 1984.

_____. *Attila the Angry.* New York: Holiday, 1985.

Simon, Norma. *How Do I Feel?* Niles, Ill.: Whitman, 1970.

_____. *I Was So Mad!* Niles, Ill.: Whitman, 1974.

Skorpen, Liesel. *His Mother's Dog.* New York: Harper, 1978.

Wittels, Harriet, and Joan Greisman. *Things I Hate!* New York: Human Sciences Press, 1973.

Zolotow, Charlotte. *The Quarreling Book.* New York: Harper, 1963.

_____. *The Hating Book.* New York: Harper, 1969.

_____. *It's Not Fair.* New York: Harper, 1976.

Lesson 5

Berenstain, Stan and Jan. *The Berenstain Bears and the Double Dare.* New York: Random, 1988.

Hazen, Barbara. *Just Say No.* Golden Look-Look Books. New York, Western Publishing, 1991.

Murphy, Elspeth. *Sometimes I'm Good, Sometimes I'm Bad.* Weston, Ont./Elgin, Ill.: Cook, 1981.

LESSON 1: EACH ONE UNIQUE

Preparation/Materials

- For making silhouettes:
  large sheet of black construction paper, one
      per student
  large sheet of white construction paper, one
      per student
  overhead projector or other source of light
  colored pencils or markers, class supply
- Songs of praise. (See step 5 for suggestions.)

Objectives

- Students will recognize that God created
  each person unique.
- Students will identify their own unique gifts
  and/or interests.
- Students will recognize and appreciate the
  diversity of class members.

Background

The self-esteem movement has been the
center of vigorous debate in recent years. Floods
of articles, books, and films have been produced
on the importance of a positive self-image and
the disastrous results of a negative self-image.
And Wayne Joosse, in *The Christian's Self-Image:
Issues and Implications,* points out that Christians
have climbed onto the self-esteem bandwagon.
They see in the movement a synthesis of biblical
truth and psychological health that offers a
long-overdue correction to the negative "such a
worm as I" image of the self. Other Christians,
however, resist promoting self-esteem. In their
view, promoting self-esteem is promoting pride
and ignoring "the worm"—the sin— in each of
us. They charge that the self-esteem movement
exemplifies the narcissism of North American
culture.

Although clearly Christians must critically
evaluate the self-esteem movement, there is
little question that how children see themselves
is extremely important. Educators have found a
direct relationship between self-esteem and success in school. And health educators have found
that children with poor self-concept are more
likely to take part in unhealthy and risky behaviors. Teachers are abdicating their responsibility
if they ignore the importance of self-esteem.
Indeed, teachers along with parents are the ones
chiefly responsible for shaping self-image in
young children.

This lesson provides a framework for creating a classroom in which student differences
are recognized and accepted. Tell students,
"God created each of you in his image. You are
God's child, and God loves you just the way
you are."

• •

Lesson

1. Open the lesson by telling students about a few activities you enjoy, or identify a few
   things that you're good at. Include at least one thing that you've enjoyed doing since
   you were young or one gift you discovered when you were young and then developed.

2. Have students work individually to identify and then to list specific activities they
   enjoy, skills they are developing, or things they're good at (for example, fixing things,
   making things, amusing younger children, singing, swimming, telling stories).

3. Make silhouettes of class members. Attach large sheets of black paper to the wall and use an overhead projector or other source of light to project students' silhouettes onto the paper. After tracing the silhouettes, have students cut them out and mount them on white paper. Next, ask students to refer to the lists they made in step 2, and write on the white background (in colored pencil or marker) the things they're good at or the activities they like.

    Alternative option: outline each student's body on large sheets of butcher paper, and have students write the lists on the body shape.

4. **Circle talk.** Use the finished silhouettes and lists to spark a discussion of the uniqueness of each individual. Gather the class into an informal circle. Briefly talk about each silhouette and highlight one or two things about the person. In the discussion, review the following concepts: God created people in his image, and thus people have a special place in creation; according to God's plan, each person is unique, with individual characteristics, interests, skills, and gifts. God gives us unique skills and gifts so that we can bless others and serve God. Ask students to identify how their specific skills or talents could be a blessing to the class, school, or wider community. Note the connection between an individual's interests and the occupation he or she may choose later in life.

    Display the silhouettes or body shapes in the classroom or school hallway.

5. Praise and thank God for creating us. Sing songs such as "Who Made Ocean, Earth, and Sky?" (*Children's Hymnbook,* 11), "There's No One Exactly Like Me" (*Songs to Grow On,* 57), "I'm Glad" (*Proclaim Songbook 1,* 14), "The Butterfly Song" (*Songs to Grow On,* 58; *Songs of God's Love,* 58), "In the Beginning" (*Psalter Hymnal,* 151).

6. **Closure.** Tell the class that this unit is called "Finding Out About Yourself and Others." Ask: "What did you find out about yourself today? What did you find out about others?"

• •

Related Activities

1. Make a "What I Wish" audio recording. At a center, record children telling what they wish they could do and why. Let the class enjoy listening to the completed recording. Consider sharing the recording with another class.

2. Have students draw pictures of themselves doing a favorite activity. On the opposite side of the paper, they may draw a picture of a goal for the future, possibly related to their unique interest or skill.

3. Listen to the song "My Favorite Things" from *The Sound of Music.* Make up new verses listing favorite things of class members. ("Chocolate chip cookies and big red strawberries/sitting by campfires and listening to stories/birthdays and picnics and fun songs to sing/these are a few of my favorite things.")

4. Follow up on step 6 with a language arts activity. Provide one or more sentence starters for class members to finish. Examples:
    Today I learned …
    I can bless others by …
    (Name) can bless me by …

LESSON 2: I FEEL...

Preparation/Materials

- Make two puppets for use throughout the year in health class. Sock puppets may be the easiest to make and manipulate. Use a different color for each puppet; add distinctive facial features and hair.
- Plan/practice a puppet script (see lesson steps 1 and 2).
- For student puppets:
  Student Activity
  Felt or midweight non-fusible (sew-in type) interfacing material such as Pellon, two 8" by 11" pieces for each student
  large-eye needles and #10 sewing thread or stapler
  Make several cardboard patterns using the puppet shape on the activity page. Students trace the pattern onto their material and then cut out the two puppet pieces. If puppets are made of felt, have students sew the pieces together.
  If puppets are of interfacing, either sew or staple the two sections together (a quick method, but success depends on staples and weight of material).
  Have students decorate the puppets and add facial features. Glue fabric and yarn remnants on felt. Use colored markers to draw features on interfacing.

Objectives

- Students will review four main feelings.
- Students will recognize that feelings are an important part of each person.
- Students will realize that feelings influence actions.
- Students will recognize that different people may feel differently about a particular situation.

Background

Because puppetry is an ideal way to present many of the situations dealt with in health, we are suggesting that you make two "health" puppets, one boy and one girl. Try to create a distinctive personality for each puppet. Make the puppets into class friends, humorous or wise commentators, or cheerful comforters. And consider using them outside of health class to resolve problems that may arise between students. Of course, if you find puppets difficult to use, you may prefer to act out the scenes yourself or rely more heavily on children's literature.

As you teach these lessons on emotions, keep in mind that some people are more emotionally expressive than others. Children will also differ in their expressiveness, but typically they are not burdened with as many inhibitions as adults and feel freer to express their emotions. However, older children or adults who are uncomfortable with open expressions of fear or sadness may squelch this freedom, admonishing young children not to cry ("Big boys/girls don't cry") or not to be afraid ("Scaredy cat!"). Therefore stress that when something sad happens, it's fitting to cry and that when something scary happens, it's okay to be afraid.

One emotion that is particularly difficult to deal with is anger. Anger is a disturbing emotion. It's so disturbing that we tend to think of it as a purely negative and destructive. But anger has a positive side. Anger over unjust treatment, for example, can become a catalyst for change. Anger can move us to confront prejudice or demand justice. We know, however, that unbridled expression of anger, with no attempt at resolution, breeds more anger. And the Bible specifically warns about the destructiveness of runaway anger. We know, too, that repressed or unresolved anger simmering within can lead to actual physical illness. Thus, lead students to realize that it's okay to feel and express anger, but also help them to identify healthy and responsible ways of expressing anger.

• •

Lesson (2 sessions)

1. Introduce the health puppets Chris and Alex (or other names of your choice). Review concepts of individual uniqueness covered in the previous lesson by having the puppets look out over the class and comment on the wonderful diversity they see. Then have them identify their own individual characteristics.

   Script idea (substitute actual puppet colors, etc.):
   Chris: I see you're bright blue with red eyes. Wow!
   Alex: And you're all green. I like your black hair and orange eyes.
   Chris: Well, we may be different colors, but we're both just plain socks.
   Alex: Yeah, you're right. We're kind of alike. My hair is yarn—just like your yours is.
   Chris (to the class): Can you see any other way we're alike?
   Lead into the lesson topic by having the puppets remark that people are also alike in many different ways, and then ask the class to identify ways in which people are alike (include that all have feelings).

2. Review the four basic emotions identified on earlier grade levels—happiness, sadness, fear, and anger. Act out the feelings using Chris and Alex. Interrupt as narrator to give information about what's going on.

   Script idea:
   Chris is sitting on her front porch steps with her dog, Prince. She's having a good time blowing bubbles. Alex comes along and joins her.
   Chris: Hi, Alex!
   Alex: Hi, Chris! That looks like fun. Can I make bubbles, too?
   Chris: Sure. Here you can use this bubblemaker. Look at all the colors in the bubble!
   Alex: Hey, that's a huge bubble! Let me pop it. (He pops the bubble, and Prince gets excited and starts barking.)
   Chris (blowing another big bubble): Prince, c'mon. Get it. Prince, come back here! Alex, help me catch him. When he gets excited, he starts chasing cars. Oh no, he's running into the street. He'll get run over! (Chris and Alex run toward the street and catch the dog.)
   Chris: Bad dog! You could have gotten killed! (Alex and Chris go back to the porch and settle Prince down.)
   Alex (sadly): You know I had a dog. Not a big dog like Prince. Just a little dog.
   Chris: I didn't know that. What was it called?
   Alex: Muffie. It was a she. She was a little white dog.
   Chris: What happened to her?
   Alex: Well, when we moved into the apartment we couldn't keep her. We had to give her away.
   Chris: You can come over and play with Prince if you like. Okay, Prince? Let's go in the backyard and throw the ball for Prince to fetch.

Alternative options: If you prefer, use only one puppet. Engage Chris in dialogue and have her tell you about what happened. Interrupt to ask questions, to make comments, or to ask the class how they think Chris was feeling. Or instead of using puppets, act out the situation yourself, taking on the role of Chris and changing the last part of the script so that Chris sadly remembers Muffie, a previous pet who was killed by a car.

3. Ask class members to identify the feelings of the puppets at various points in the narrative. (The happy and enjoyable feelings at the beginning of the dialogue change when the dog runs into the street. Chris is afraid that the dog will be run over, and she's angry at the dog. Alex is sad remembering the pet dog he used to have. Chris offers sympathy, and they both cheer up.) Spend some time talking about each feeling. Why did the characters feel the way they did? Ask: "Which feelings are pleasant? Which feelings do you think are unpleasant?" Note that anger may not be pleasant, but it's not wrong or bad to be angry.

4. Review the basic facial expressions and other body language that usually accompany each feeling. Ask volunteers to show (pantomiming only) how they might feel if they were
   - going on picnic.
   - trying to learn how to roller skate, but kept on falling down.
   - praised for doing a job well.
   - lost because they wandered away from parents at a mall or other public place.
   - told they couldn't go along with parents or siblings on an outing.
   - accidentally knocked down on the playground.
   - deliberately knocked down on the playground.
   - eating their favorite food.
   - blamed for something they didn't do.
   - being chased by a swarm of bees.
   - given a dollar by a family friend.

   These are simple situations to evoke immediate responses; do the exercise quickly. Then have the class discuss the type of body language usually accompanying each feeling. Do we think about our body language or is it automatic? ("What do we do with our hands when we're mad? With our face? How do we act when we're afraid of something?")

5. Discuss how feelings influence actions. Refer to the situations in step 2 or step 4 and have students predict how feelings will influence subsequent actions. (Or ask: How did Chris's feelings for Prince influence her actions? How did they influence her offer to Alex?) It's important to make clear that even though feelings influence our actions, we are not free to let our actions blindly follow our feelings. We are to express feelings in a responsible way. For example, though it's not bad to get angry, we're not free to express our anger any way we want. For example, we aren't free to hurt others, break things, or disrupt the whole class.

6. **Student activity.** Help students make their own puppets, following the steps suggested in Preparations/Materials. Consider asking a parent or older student to assist with this activity. To save classroom time, you may wish to trace the patterns onto the material before class. Having a sample puppet for the class to use as a model will also be helpful.

Another option is to have the children sit in a circle and speak through their puppets to talk about feelings. Tell students: "Today we're talking about feeling happy, sad, afraid, and angry. What are some things that make us—and our puppets—happy, sad, afraid, and angry? Let's start by thinking about what makes us happy." Students can then take turns briefly introducing and showing their puppets to the rest of the class and then speaking through their puppets to complete the sentence "I feel (happy/sad/angry/afraid) when ..." If the class is small, go around the circle four times, once for each emotion; if the class is large, switch the emotion about every three to five students, and have each child complete a sentence for one emotion. At the beginning of the activity explain the rules: show respect by listening to each other, no put downs are allowed, and passing is each student's right. At the end of the activity give students who passed the opportunity to respond if they wish.

If time is limited, you may wish to have students in pairs informally use their puppets to act out situations in which one or more of the basic four feelings are expressed. Ask a few volunteer pairs to present their situation for the rest of the class.

Since the class will also be using the puppets in the next lesson, store them in a convenient location.

7. **Closure.** Reflect on the lesson with questions such as the following:
   - "Was it hard for you to think about what to say with your puppet?"
   - "What were some similarities/differences in feelings?"
   - "Do our feelings change? Why do you think they change? Can you imagine what it would be like if our feelings never changed?"

Tell students that in the next lesson they'll be talking about feelings again and using their puppets again.

Related Activities

1. Enjoy reading poetry that expresses different feelings. Consider writing a poem on chart paper and using the poem for a class choral reading. "The Wrong Start" by Marchette Chute, "Wiggly Giggles" by Stacy Crossen and Natalie Covell, "Sulk" and "Leave Me Alone" by Felice Holman, "Keziah" by Gwendolyn Brooks, and "The Runaway" by Bobbi Katz (in *The Random House Book of Poetry for Children*) are poems all dealing with common feelings of children.

2. Make a class book entitled "We Get Angry When ..." Have each child contribute one page to the booklet by writing one sentence identifying something that makes him or her angry and then drawing or painting an

accompanying illustration. Gather the pages and put them together in a book. When you read the book with the class, identify appropriate ways to act in each situation. Consider making a booklet for each of the basic feelings.

3. Read the classic by Judith Viorst, *Alexander and the Terrible, Horrible, No Good, Very Bad Day.* Have each student write a similar story from experience with himself or herself as the main character. Or suggest variations such as *(Name) and the Scary, Alarming, Frightening, Most Spooky Day,* or *(Name) and the Not So Happy, Down in the Dumps, Everything's Wrong, Very Sad Day,* or *(Name) and the Awesome, Wonderful, Most Fantastic, Better than Ever Day.*

4. Global awareness: Is body language similar the world over? Identify different types of body language associated with greetings (waving, nodding, bowing, shaking handing, kissing on both cheeks, and so on). What feeling do most greetings express? Consider inviting someone from the community to tell students about body language of another culture. Or integrate the topic of body language with current social studies.

LESSON 3: COMMUNICATING FEELINGS

Preparation/Materials

- Obtain a story or poem about feelings or plan a puppet script in which one puppet feels left out.
- Student puppets from previous lesson
- Optional: Health puppet Alex
- Optional: chart paper

Objectives

- Students will identify a variety of feelings.
- Students will identify ways to know how others are feeling.
- Students will practice asking about others' feelings.
- Students will understand the importance of communicating their feelings to others and to God.

• •

Lesson

1. This lesson may be introduced in one of two ways. Read a story or poem in which the characters express one or more feelings associated with a basic feeling students have previously identified. For example, read a book in which the characters are lonely, jealous, hurt, or worried. Suggested titles:

    Time to Go by Beverly and David Fiday or *Jim's Dog Muffins* by Miriam Cohen—sadness

    Jim Meets the Thing by Miriam Cohen or *Franklin in the Dark* by Paulette Bourgeois—fear

    His Mother's Dog by Liesel Skorpen, *It's Not Fair* by Charlotte Zolotow or *She Come Bringing Me That Little Baby Girl* by Eloise Greenfield—jealousy

    The Trip by Ezra Jack Keats or *We Are Best Friends* by Aliki—loneliness

    Ira Says Goodbye and *Lyle and the Birthday Party* by Bernard Waber—sadness and envy

    Or use the puppet Alex to introduce a variety of feelings such as being disappointed, left out, worried, and hurt.

    Script idea:

    Alex is alone and moping in his backyard. ("I'm never going to ask Chris to come over and play again.") Encourage students to ask questions to find out about the situation. Alex explains that he asked Chris to come over and play and have lunch at his house. When they were playing a game together in the backyard, Jamie came over and before long Chris went off to play ball with Jamie.

    Ask students to identify the main character's feelings in the story or puppet play. Explain that we have many feelings besides happiness, anger, fear, and sadness.

2. Encourage the students to name as many other feelings as they can come up with. Write the words on the board or on a chart. If possible, note which of the main feelings

each feeling is associated with. To help students, you may wish to briefly suggest situations in which these feelings may occur.

Suggested feelings to include:

calm	embarrassed	worried	loving	disappointed
confused	silly	ashamed	joyful	frustrated
lonely	surprised	mean	excited	jealous

(Be sure to include the first two words on the list because they appear on the student activity of Lesson 4.)

Keep the chart of words to use in language arts activities.

3. **Discussion.** Briefly recall the connection of facial expression and other body language to feelings. Explain that usually people can guess our feelings by looking at us and listening to us, and sometimes we can guess other people's feelings by looking at them and listening to them. But sometimes it's not so easy to tell. Ask: "How can others be sure they know what we're feeling? Or how can we be sure we know what others are feeling?" (By asking.)

Talk about the importance of sharing ourselves with others: "When we're excited or happy about something, telling others often adds to the happiness and makes others happy, too. And when we're unhappy, telling others (parents, other family members, good friends) often helps us feel better. God created us this way; God created us to live with others and share ourselves with others." Stress the importance and the comfort of talking to God about our feelings when we pray.

4. **Student activity.** Have the class use the puppets they made in Lesson 2 to act out situations reflecting a variety of emotions. Divide the class into pairs or small groups for the activity. Give each group a feeling or situation to act out for the rest of the class. Give them time to practice their presentation. The rest of the class guesses and then asks what the feeling is. Or refer to the story or puppet skit used at the beginning of the lesson. Have students act out different ways for the main character to deal with the situation.

Collect the puppets and keep them for use in subsequent health lessons.

5. **Closure.** Summarize and evaluate with questions such as the following:
   * "How many different feelings can you name?"
   * "How do we know how another person is feeling?"
   * "What's good about sharing our feelings with others?"
   * "Why should we to talk to God about our feelings?"

Related Activities

1. Make an audio recording of the step 1 story (or another story in which feelings are described or expressed) for a center. Students can listen to the story and follow along in the book or use their puppets to act it out.

2. Read verses from the Psalms to show how David or other psalmists talked to God about their feelings. (In Psalm 142, for example, David is tired and lonely and tells God about his trouble.) Or read a book from the series *David and I Talk to God* by Elspeth Murphy.

3. Write the new feelings words and their definitions on separate sets of tagboard cards. Use the cards for various center activities such as matching exercises and filling in missing words in sentence strips.

4. Tap the wide variety of children's literature on the subject of emotions. Make books about feelings available in the class library or reading center. Read some of these suggested titles with the class:
   God Cares When I'm Feeling Mean by Elspeth Murphy
   Bartholomew the Bossy and *Attila the Angry* by Marjorie Sharmat
   A Miracle for Sarah by Regine Schindler
   Things I Hate! by Harriet Wittels and Joan Greisman
   The Hating Book and *It's Not Fair* by Charlotte Zolotow
   I Was So Mad!, *How Do I Feel?*, and *I Am Not a Crybaby* by Norma Simon
   Nobody Plays With a Cabbage by Meindert DeJong

LESSON 4: DEVELOPING EMPATHY

Preparation/Materials

- Student Activity
- Paper fasteners, one per student
- Piece of string or yarn about 8" long, one piece for each student
- Provide pictures of children in a variety of situations (sick in bed or with limb in a cast, sitting alone on steps or swing, running away from something, flying a kite). If possible, have one picture for every pair or group of students.
- Write the poem "Changing" on chart paper.
- Optional: props for student roleplays

Objectives

- Students will develop empathy for others.
- Students will identify ways to respond to others' feelings.

Background

Only as children mature both intellectually and emotionally can they begin to see a situation from another's point of view. "One way," says Mary Vander Goot, "to encourage children to take social responsibility for their own actions is to teach them to identify the consequences of their emotional expressions on others." Encouraging empathy is the best way to help students learn to be considerate of each other. As you discuss various situations in this lesson, help students consider how they would feel if they were in a similar situation and how they would like to be helped or treated.

Lesson

1. **Student activity.** Ask students to cut out the circle and pointer and attach the pointer in the center of the circle with a fastener. Help children identify the feeling each picture depicts starting at the top and moving to the right: feeling afraid, happy, sad, calm, upset or angry, and confused).

2. **Discussion.** Gather students into a discussion circle. Each should have the completed feeling circle in hand. Ask students to show on their circles how they feel right now. Give volunteers opportunity to talk about why they feel the way they do. (Be sensitive to students' right to privacy during this activity.)

   Then show pictures of children in a variety of situations. After showing each picture, have students individually decide how the pictured child is feeling and locate the feeling on the circle. Did the class agree on the way the pictured child is feeling? Why or why not? Ask: "How do you think you might feel in that situation?" Then together explore some ways others could help the person feel better or could share someone's happy feelings.

3. **Roleplay activity.** Divide the class into small groups, and have groups roleplay responding to others' feelings. Assign each group one of the situations discussed in step 2. If possible, give each group a picture of the situation they are to act out. Consider making some simple props available to add to the enjoyment. After each roleplay, ask

the rest of the class if they can think of other ways to respond to those in the situation pictured.

4. Have students attach a piece of string or yarn to their feelings circles and use masking tape to hang the circles from their desks or tables. During the day refer to the circles at appropriate times to reinforce or review unit concepts.

5. Read and discuss the poem "Changing" by Mary Ann Hoberman. Put up a chart of the poem, so students can follow along as you read.

> **Changing**
> I know what *I* feel like:
> I'd like to be *you*
> And feel what *you* feel like
> And do what *you* do.
> I'd like to change places
> For maybe a week
> And look like your look-alike
> And speak as you speak
> And think what you're thinking
> And go where you go
> And feel what you're feeling
> And know what you know.
> I wish we could do it;
> What fun it would be
> If I could try you out
> And you could try me.

Lead students to understand how changing places with someone else for a week might not only be fun, but might change our feelings about the person and the way we treat that person. Talk about God's command to love your neighbor as ourselves. Close the lesson with this question: "How could changing places help us to love others as ourselves?"

• •

Related Activities

1. Tell Bible stories that illustrate showing how Jesus responded to others. For example, tell the story of Zaccheus (Luke 19:1-9) or one of the many healing stories.

2. Have the class memorize the poem "Changing" or recite it as a choral reading.

3. Read stories that tie in with the lesson. Two suggestions: *What's the Matter with Car-ruthers?* by James Marshall and *Mary, Mary* by Sarah Hayes.

4. Sing songs about loving others. Suggestions: "Love God With All Your Soul" (*Children's Hymnbook,* 169), "We Love" (*Proclaim Songbook 1,* 39), "Lord, I Want to Be a Christian," verses 1, 2, and 4 (*Psalter Hymnal,* 264; *Proclaim Songbook 1,* 40).

LESSON 5: SAYING NO

Preparation/Materials

- Health puppet (Alex)
- Story on lesson topic to read to the class
- Student Activity

Objectives

- Students will identify feelings accompanying peer pressure.
- Students will choose to say no when something is harmful or wrong.

Background

This lesson explores feelings that arise when others want us to do something that we don't think we should do. Help students recognize the conflicting emotions that these situations cause and the importance of saying no to harmful peer pressure.

Lesson

1. Interact with the puppet Alex as he describes a situation in which Chris exerted pressure to try to make him do something dangerous—for example, tasting pills from a bottle standing on the kitchen counter or eating berries from a bush growing in the park. Script suggestion:

    Alex: I don't know if I should tell you this, (name of teacher). I think I will though. Something happened yesterday, and Chris is mad at me.

    Teacher: What happened?

    Alex: Chris and I were playing. Chris picked some berries from a bush and pretended to cook them, but she wanted me to really eat them.

    Teacher: What did you do?

    Interrupt the conversation and elicit from the class how Someone being pressured may feel (worried that the other person will be mad at them or they'll spoil the game if they say no; afraid of what will happen if they say yes). If you wish, have them use their feelings circles to show how they would feel in the situation. Then have Alex finish telling about the incident.

    Alex: I know eating berries can be dangerous. They might be poisonous. So I said no. But Chris was upset and said I wasn't any fun to play with. She went home.

    Ask: "What might have happened if Alex hadn't had the courage to say no?"

    Alternative option: have students act out the situation described in the puppet script.

2. **Discussion.** Follow-up with a discussion of saying no when something is dangerous and also when something is wrong (stealing or breaking others' belongings or joining others to tease another classmate are appropriate situations to discuss at this age level).

Play a game "I Can Say No." Describe various situations, and ask students how they would respond.

- "You and your friend are in the candy store. You really want some Gummi Bears, but don't have enough money with you. Your friend whispers, 'Just put them in your pocket, no one will know.' What do you say?"
- "On the playground a group of kids are teasing someone you don't like very well. Your friend runs to join them saying, 'This is our chance to get even for all the rotten things he's done to us.' What do you say?"
- "You and your friend find a really neat toy on the playground at recess. You know it belongs to Jane, but she has already gone inside. Your friend picks it up and says, 'Finders keepers, losers weepers.' What do you say?"
- "You are quietly sitting and eating your lunch. Today you have your favorite dessert. Just as you are about to bite into it, a fifth grader sits down next to you and says, 'Hand it over.' What would you say?"

In your discussion stress that God created us so that we can choose. Making right choices can help keep us and others safe. And doing what is right, obeying God, is more important than what others think of us. Assure children, though, that when we do make a wrong choice or do something wrong, God forgives us if we're sorry and helps us do better the next time.

3. **Student Activity.** Students are to tell how to say no when something (1) is wrong, (2) is dangerous, (3) might hurt another, or (4) might harm their body in some way. Briefly talk about these four categories. How would answers be different? The same?

   If creating the sentences is difficult for your class, consider brainstorming possible sentences, writing them on the board, and then having students choose which sentences they wish to write down.

   The sentences should have an assertive tone but not be rude or combative.

   Give students time to write about a time when they said no.

4. **Closure:** "Why is it hard to say no sometimes? What is the difference between saying 'I can't' and 'I won't'?" (Explore when each response is appropriate.)

5. **Unit closure.** End the unit with a lively, affirming activity. (The first two suggestions are adapted from *Friendly Classroom for a Small Planet*.)
   - *Here's a Clap.* The class focuses on each child by turn with the following chant:
     Here's a clap 'cause we're glad you're here. (clap)
     Here's a clap for a special kid. (clap)
     Here's a clap for (name). (applause)
   - *Word Tickler.* When children say positive things about each other, they "tickle" each other with words. Students can pair up for the exercise, taking turns saying three

nice things about each other. (Stress these should be honest, positive comments.) Or, if the class is very comfortable with this type of exercise, gather the children in a circle and have each child say something positive about his or her neighbor.

- *Good Things.* Sit in a circle. Ask each student to share a positive experience of the last few days or one thing he or she liked about the unit. (Don't discuss during the sharing; and be sure students feel free to pass.) After going around the circle, talk about similarities in the experiences.
- Sing "There's No One Exactly Like Me" (*Songs to Grow On,* 57) or "The Butterfly Song" (*Songs to Grow On,* 58; Proclaim Songbook 1, 14; *Songs of God's Love,* 58).

●●●

Related Activities

1. Tell Bible stories that relate to the lesson theme: Noah building the ark, Joseph in the house of Potiphar, Daniel and his three friends at the court in Babylon. However, bear in mind that the Bible also has stories of those who failed under similar pressure: Abram passing off Sarai as his sister, Aaron building the golden calf, and Peter denying Christ.

2. Students can use the puppets from the previous lesson to act out the Chris and Alex situation or the story they read in step 3.

3. Read a story to the class or tell a true story that reinforces lesson concepts. Two book suggestions are *The Berenstain Bears and the Double Dare* by Stan and Jan Berenstain and *Just Say No* by Barbara Hazen.

Ups and Downs of Family Life

Goals

- Students will develop their understanding of family life—both its rough spots and its joys.
- Students will develop an understanding of gender differences and similarities.
- Students will develop a Christian perspective on death.

Background

God created us to live in relationship with others. Genesis 2 pictures God the Creator thinking over Adam's relationships and deciding that Adam needed another human being with whom to share his life. "It is not good for the man to be alone. I will make a helper suitable for him" (verse 18). Marriage and, by extension, the family are part of a loving God's plan for human life. Scripture affirms this throughout (see, for example, Psalm 127:3-4). The idea that marriage is a good gift is highlighted by the frequent use in Scripture of marriage as a metaphor of God's relationship to his people (Hosea 1-4, Isaiah 54:4-6, Mark 2:19-20, Ephesians 5:22-23, Revelation 19:7-9).

But marriage and family life have not escaped the effects of sin. Because we are sinful, we have no power within ourselves to maintain healthy family relationships. Our brokenness is reflected in family life. But in Christ we can find healing, forgiveness, and the power to restore relationships and make new beginnings.

With this Christian perspective in mind, how do we teach a unit on the family? As Christians we want to celebrate the joy of God's good gift of family, but we also must recognize the existence of common family struggles. Our homes are not trouble free and glossing over the effects of sin is not helpful to our students. The Bible is brutally honest in its picture of family life. Think of the stories about the families of Jacob, David, and Solomon. Teaching the unit in a moralistic way will only serve to make students who have troubled families feel guilty. God is present in both troubled and tranquil families. The good news is that God came to sinners, to all those with broken and contrite hearts.

Vocabulary

Integrate the following suggested vocabulary:

shelter	family	solve	tradition	commandment
food	honor	female	heritage	responsibility
clothing	forgiveness	problem	males	hope

Unit Resources

Anderson, Ray S., and Dennis B. Guernsey. *On Being Family: A Social Theology of the Family.* Grand Rapids: Eerdmans, 1985.

> The central thesis of this teacher resource is that "God has placed human persons in a created order for which the covenant love of God provides the fundamental paradigm" for the formation of family life.

Hart, Carole, and others. *Free to Be ... You and Me.* Toronto/New York: Bantam, 1972.
A collection of poems, stories, and songs that attempt to break down stereotypes and promote self-esteem.

Hoberman, Mary Ann. *Fathers, Mothers, Sisters, Brothers: A Collection of Family Poems.* Boston: Little, Brown, 1991.

Lesson Resources

Lesson 1

Dantzer-Rosenthal, Marya. *Some Things Are Different, Some Things Are the Same.* Niles, Ill., Whitman, 1986.
Compares the homes and families of two friends.

Vendrell, Carme, and J.M. Parramón. *Family: Parents.* Educational Series. Toronto/New York: Barron's, 1987.
About the role of parents in raising and caring for children and about how feelings of a child can affect a parent.

_____. *Family: Grandparents.* Educational Series. Toronto/New York: Barron's, 1987.
About the place of grandparents in the family.

Lesson 2

Cole, Joanna. *Asking About Sex and Growing Up.* New York: Morrow, 1988.

Galbraith, Kathryn. *Waiting for Jennifer.* New York: McElderry Books, 1987.

Henkes, Kevin. *Chester's Way.* New York: Greenwillow, 1988.

Hummel, Ruth. *Where Do Babies Come From?* Learning About Sex Series. St. Louis: Concordia, 1982, 1988.
Seven-year-old Suzanne learns how babies grow inside the mother and that both mother and father have a part in making a baby. Includes the following vocabulary: *uterus, navel, pregnant, vagina, vulva, penis, scrotum, testicles, sperm.* A helpful resource written from a Christian perspective and intended for children ages 6-8. One criticism: on the whole the book's approach is direct and natural, but the setting of chapter 2 in a museum is contrived.

Merriam, Eve. *Boys & Girls, Girls & Boys.* New York: Holt, 1972.

Zolotow, Charlotte. *William's Doll.* New York: Harper, 1972.
This classic about a boy who wants a doll is also available on videocassette.

Lessons 3-6

Berenstain, Stan and Jan. *The Berenstain Bears Get in a Fight.* New York: Random, 1982.
Several titles in the Berenstain Bears Series tie deal with health topics. Be aware, however, that some books in the series tend to picture the father as bumbling and ineffective.

Families and Rules: Watch How Well Everything Works. McGraw Hill and Education Services Group.
A 10-minute film about how rules help a family live together.

Girard, Linda Walvoord. *At Daddy's on Saturdays.* Morton Grove, Ill.: Whitman/Toronto: General Publishing, 1987.

Katie discovers that even though her parents live apart, she will maintain her loving relationship with her father. Students whose parents are divorced will find this book reassuring.

Getting Along at Home. South Deerfield, Mass.: Channing L. Bete.
This booklet stresses the value of communication to good family life and gives tips on handling conflict in positive ways. Available from the publisher: 200 State Rd., South Deerfield, Massachusetts 01373-0200 (phone 800-628-7733).

Hazen, Barbara. *Even If I Did Something Awful?* New York: Atheneum, 1981.

Keller, Holly. *Maxine in the Middle.* New York: Greenwillow, 1989.

McPhail, David. *Sisters.* New York: Harcourt, 1984.

Munsch, Robert. *Love You Forever.* Willowdale, Ont.: Firefly, 1982.

Prutzman, Priscilla, and others. *The Friendly Classroom for a Small Planet.* Philadelphia: New Society Publishers, 1988.
Put out by Children's Creative Response to Conflict, an organization with Quaker roots, this teacher resource contains helpful material on conflict resolution. Order from the publisher: P.O. Box 582, Santa Cruz, California 95061.

Sharmat, Marjorie. *Sometimes Papa and Mama Fight.* New York: Harper, 1980.

_____. *My Mother Never Listens to Me.* Niles, Ill.: Whitman, 1984.

Uldry, Janice. *Thump and Plunk.* New York: Harper, 1981.

Zolotow, Charlotte. *If It Weren't for You.* New York: Harper, 1966.

_____. *Timothy Too.* Boston: Houghton, 1986.

Lesson 6
Kopp, Ruth. *Where Has Grandpa Gone?* Grand Rapids: Zondervan, 1983.
Written from a Christian perspective, this teacher resource describes how a child perceives death at various age levels and gives suggestions for guiding children through times of loss. Includes a read-aloud section to help explain the meaning of death to children.

The following is a list of K-2 student resources.

Books about the death of animals or pets

Brown, Margaret Wise. *The Dead Bird.* Reprint of 1958 edition. New York: HarperCollins, 1989.

Cohen, Miriam. *Jim's Dog Muffins.* New York: Greenwillow, 1984.

Keller, Holly. *Goodbye, Max.* New York: Greenwillow, 1984.

Sanford, Doris. *It Must Hurt a Lot: A Child's Book About Death.* Portland, Ore.: Multnomah, 1986.

Stock, Catherine. *Better With Two.* New York: Harper, 1988.

Wahl, Mats. *Grandfather's Laika.* Minneapolis: Carolrhoda Books, 1990.

Books dealing with moving and change or loss

Aliki. *We Are Best Friends.* New York: Greenwillow, 1982.

Hickman, Martha. *My Friend William Moved Away.* Nashville, Tenn.: Abingdon, 1979.

Hughes, Shirley. *Moving Molly.* New York: Lothrop, 1988.

Sharmat, Marjorie. *Mitchell Is Moving.* New York: Macmillan, 1978.

Waber, Bernard. *Ira Says Goodbye.* Boston: Houghton, 1988.

Zolotow, Charlotte. *Janey.* New York: Harper, 1973.

Books dealing with human death

Clifton, Lucille. *Everett Anderson's Goodbye.* New York: Holt, 1983.
Everett grieves for his dead father. The book begins with a list of the five stages of grieving and follows Everett through each stage of grief.

Cohn, Janice. *I Had a Friend Named Peter:* Talking to Children About Death. New York: Morrow, 1987.

de Paola, Tomie. *Nana Upstairs, Nana Downstairs.* New York: Puffin, 1973.

Egger, Bettina. *Marianne's Grandmother.* New York: Dutton, 1987.

Gould, Deborah. *Grandpa's Slide Show.* New York: Lothrop, 1987.

Kaldhol, Marit, and Wenche Oyen. *Goodbye Rune.* New York: Kane/Miller, 1987.

LESSON 1: FAMILIES PROVIDE FOR NEEDS

Preparation/Materials
- Student Activities 1a and 1b
- Student Activity 2
- Note: Lesson 6 of this unit centers on family heritage and traditions. Each student is requested to bring from home some object tied to his or her heritage. We suggest teachers send a note to parents with the request at the beginning of the unit to provide ample time.

Objectives
- Students will be aware that living in families is part of God's plan.
- Students will identify ways their family provides for them.
- Students will choose to thank God for their family.

Background
"God established marriage and, by extension, the family as a cornerstone of creation," states *Horizons Health's* statement of philosophy. In this lesson, lead students to understand that the family is part of God's loving design for the human race and awaken in them an appreciation of the blessings of family life.

As you teach this unit, be sensitive to students who may find the subject of family life painful because of divorce, death, or other circumstances. Be aware that there may be family tensions that no one knows about. If a student is reluctant to carry out a specific assignment, find an alternate activity.

• •

Lesson

1. Ask students to identify what a family is. (A simple definition: your family is made up of people who are related to you). Make clear that many different groupings comprise what we call a family and that family members don't always live together (college age students away from home, etc.).

2. Discuss the origin and purpose of the family. Ask: "How did the family begin? Why do you think God planned for human beings to live in families?" Then ask: "How does your family help you? What are some of the things you receive from your family?"

   Use Student Activities 1a and 1b to identify the basic needs that are met by families: food, shelter, clothing, love, help, and learning about God. Have students look carefully at the picture and identify how adult family members are helping children. Point out not only what the family members are doing in the pictures but also the beds, pillows, blankets, food, warmth of the house, washing facilities for clothing, materials for the project in process. Bring out the need each person has for comfort and love and support. What pictures in the visual show family members giving love? If time allows, have the students cut out and color the pictures. Fasten them together with tape.

   Lead a discussion on what Christian parents also do to teach their children about God. Elicit from students how parents do this (reading the Bible, praying, talking about how to serve God, going to Sunday School and church.)

3. As part of the class session or during class devotions, thank God for giving us families who care for us and teach us about God. An appropriate prayer song is "For the Beauty of the Earth" (*Psalter Hymnal,* 432), especially verse 3, which refers to the family.

4. **Student activity.** Using Student Activity 2, have students identify the basic need each picture depicts and choose the word from the word bank that matches the picture. Review the lesson ideas as you go over the completed activity with the class. Close the lesson by giving a brief preview of topics to be covered in the unit.

• •

Related Activities

1. Center activity: have students make cards or paper plate wall hangers expressing thanks and love to families for providing for them.

2. Make a bulletin board depicting class members' families. Ask students to bring photographs or draw pictures of their families. Display the pictures side by side and on top of each other as if they are rooms in a house. Make a paper roof with the heading "The Family of God."

3. Have students make collages picturing different family groupings.

4. Have students discuss and write about how someone in their family depends on them.

LESSON 2: BEING BOYS AND GIRLS

Preparation/Materials
- Health puppet or puppets
- Plan details of the puppet script.
- Story or poem to read on relationships/ similarities of boys and girls
- Student Activity
- Optional: Teacher Visual for teaching names of body parts (Unit 6, Lesson 5)

Objectives
- Students will understand that human sexuality is a gift of God.
- Students will understand that according to God's plan both fathers and mothers have a part in beginning a baby.
- Students will consider gender differences and similarities.

Background
God has designed us as sexual creatures. Our sexuality has purpose and meaning. As males and females we have physically different bodies, but our sexuality is much more than that. Our sexuality has to do with who we are as males and females, with how we understand our sexual selves. Our life experiences shape that understanding. And, perhaps most important of all, our understanding is reflected in our daily relationships with each other.

Of course, although sexuality cannot be equated with the sex act, the sex act is a part of our sexuality. According to God's plan, the creation of new life is one of the purposes of our sexuality. Giving accurate information and using correct terms as we describe the process of creating new life shows respect for God's gift of sexuality. As one author says, "Because God is certainly not embarrassed that we are sexual creatures, neither should we be."

Providing accurate information about sexuality in developmentally appropriate ways from kindergarten on creates the same kind of foundation for later learning that schools provide in math or language. Specialists in the field of family life education warn that if elementary schools sidestep the issue, sex education at higher levels becomes a struggle to overcome years of accumulated misinformation. Besides, our culture surrounds children from a young age with improper views of sex and sexuality. Teaching children from a young age that sexuality is God's gift to be used in a way God intends will provide children with the Christian perspective they vitally need.

Be sure to inform parents in advance about what will be covered in this lesson. Good communication establishes trust and prevents misunderstandings. Schools may wish to discuss the specific content of health education at the orientation meetings at the beginning of the school year.

Lesson
1. Have a dialogue with Alex (or set up a dialogue between Chris and Alex) dealing with gender differences. Together you decide on a game to play indoors on a rainy or cold day. When you decide to play house, Alex wants to be the mother. You object and tell him that he can pretend to be the mother for the fun of it, but he can't really be the mother. Interrupt the dialogue to ask the class who is right. Why can't boys be mothers? When a girl grows up, she will have a body like her mother, and a boy will have a body like his father. This is part of God's plan: all people are created either *male*

or *female* (teach the words as new vocabulary). Explain that being born as boys or girls is a special gift of God.

As you continue the dialogue, have the puppet ask you or the class why God made people of both sexes or why mothers are one sex and fathers another. Explain that a mother's body is different from a father's body. It takes both a mother and a father to start a baby. God planned it this way. Every baby starts when two small parts join together and then grow. One part comes from the mother's body (egg) and one part from the father's body (sperm). So the baby belongs to both the mother and the father. They both have a part in starting the baby. You may wish to add that God made male and female bodies so that they fit together in a special way. The sperm from the father enters the mother's body. When the sperm and egg meet, a new baby starts. Then the baby grows inside the mother until it's time to be born. (How much detail you include here will depend on your school's sex education policy.)

Consider using the teacher visual of the human body used in Unit 6, Lesson 5, to teach or review names of male and female body parts. Specifically explain the father's and mother's role in making a baby by stating that the father's penis puts the sperm in the mother's vagina (an opening in the mother's body near the vulva pictured).

Alternate option: read appropriate sections from the book *Where Do Babies Come From?* by Ruth Hummel (Concordia Learning About Sex Series).

Have Alex identify some things he does/uses every day that's different from a girl (wears different clothes, uses a separate washroom at school, perhaps has a separate room at home from his sister).

2. Involve the class in a discussion of similarities between boys and girls. Lead students to understand that boys and girls are different in some ways, but they can do many similar things. Help break down stereotypical views of male/female abilities, personality traits, and vocational choices.

3. Follow up by reading a story or poem that reinforces lesson concepts. *Free to Be ... You and Me*, developed by Marlo Thomas and others, contains several poems (for example, "What Are Little Boys Made Of?" and "My Dog Is a Plumber") that challenge gender stereotypes. Other possible titles are Eve Merriam's *Boys & Girls, Girls & Boys*, Charlotte Zolotow's *William's Doll* (book or film) and Kevin Henkes' *Chester's Way*.

4. **Student activity.** Pair up students to interview each other about interests and likes. (You may have to pair up with a student if the class has an odd number of students.) Turn to the worksheet in the student workbook and explain the activity. If necessary, read the questions with the class.

Have students present their interviews. One option is to read the questions one at a time and ask class members to read their answers. Discuss the results. Are answers diverse or do many students like the same things? Is there a boy/girl pattern to some answers? If so, discuss possible reasons for the patterns.

Another option is to tabulate and graph the answers. What patterns emerge? Are patterns gender based? If so, talk about causes or reasons. If not, note and discuss that fact.

5. **Closure:** "God created human beings as male and female, as boys and girls. Although some parts of the male body and female body are different, many parts are the same. (Have children name similar parts.) Male and female or father and mother both have a part in making a baby, but we know, too, that God is the one who gives the baby life. That's a mystery and a miracle! Another thing to remember is that boys and girls and men and women are equally God's children. And we are all called to serve and love God."

• •

Related Activities

1. Discuss how families prepare for the arrival of a new baby. Ask an expectant mother to talk about what she and other family members are doing to get ready for the baby.

2. Integrate with language arts. Have students write two or three sentences in their journals about why they like being a girl or a boy.

3. Write poems or a class poem entitled "What Are Little Children Made of, Made of?" First read and talk about the classic nursery rhymes:

What are little girls made of, made of?
What are little girls made of?
Sugar and spice and all that's nice.
That's what little girls are made of.

What are little boys made of, made of?
What are little boys made of?
Frogs and snails and puppy dog tails.
That's what little boys are made of.

Then write poems in the same patterns, emphasizing things children have in common.

LESSON 3: RESOLVING CONFLICTS IN THE FAMILY

Preparation/Materials

- Ask two class members to stage a disagreement during the class period. At the beginning of the class session, invite them to choose a book to read or a game or toy to use. Have them both choose the same object.
- Student Activity

Objectives

- Students will understand the concept of conflict.
- Students will evaluate ways of resolving conflicts.
- Students will develop conflict resolution skills.

Background

Children need to know that even loving families sometimes disagree with each other. Conflicts are a "natural" part of life on this planet, especially between people who are with each other for many hours each day and share the same time, space, and objects. And children need reassurance that conflicts do not mean that family members don't love each other.

However, unresolved conflicts are harmful. They can harm a person's physical, social, emotional, and spiritual health. God instructs us to "take care of our wrath." This is not only a good biblical principle, it is a good health principle, too. Unresolved conflict causes stress and stress-related illnesses. And the anger and bitterness that results from unresolved conflict affects our relationship with God, creating distance between us and God.

"Blessed are the peacemakers." This scriptural directive approaches the reason for resolving conflict from a different direction. God desires that we live in peace and that we, relying on God's grace and the power of the Spirit, become peacemakers. Nurturing children in the skills and attitudes of peace is kingdom-building work. Instilling in children the desire to be peacemakers is a first step.

How do we teach children to resolve conflicts? First, avoid handing down solutions. Instead, stimulate students to look for creative solutions and join them in the search. A spirit of cooperation in looking for a solution reinforces the value of cooperation—a necessary ingredient of conflict resolution. Second, encourage students to recognize and try to understand the feelings of those involved in the disagreement. Third, have the students attempt to identify the underlying cause of the conflict. Sometimes feelings run so high that the real cause is buried. Since lack of effective communication is often a contributing factor, stress the importance of good two-way communication in resolving many conflicts.

At this grade level, the two lessons focusing on conflict resolution have been placed in the family living unit. However, the material could be moved to the next unit and taught in the context of the school or of the wider community. Bear in mind, however, that lessons focusing on conflict resolution will be taught in that wider context in grade 3.

Lesson (1-2 sessions)

1. Begin the lesson with the pre-arranged roleplay of an argument. End the conflict by taking the object away from the students and asking them to sit down. (If you prefer, use the health puppets to demonstrate the conflict situations.)

2. Ask other class members what happened and why. (The students fought or argued because both wanted the same thing.) Define and teach the word *conflict* to the class. Ask: "How did the conflict end?" (Teacher took the object away.) Have students identify common family conflicts they have had that ended in a similar way. (Two children fight over a game, and a parent takes game away; they fight over which TV program to watch, and parents turn off the TV.) Also identify what feelings these situations caused. Tell students that even though family members love and help each other, they sometimes also disagree.

3. Roleplay the opening situation again. This time have the two students try to solve their problem. Consider following these steps:
   1. Have the two parties sit down facing each other. Ask each to tell his or her side without interruption. You may help the participants understand and empathize with the other side.
   2. Ask the two parties to brainstorm ideas on how to solve the problem. (If you wish, also ask the class for suggestions.)
   3. Have the disputants decide which solution they can agree on. (Ownership of the solution should always belong to the people involved in the conflict, not what the larger group thinks "is the best ending.")

4. Roleplay other conflicts and follow the same formula as in Step 3 for resolution. Use the following suggested situations and/or others the students suggest.
   • Siblings A and B are playing with a toy that belongs to A. B starts roughhousing and the toy breaks. A wants B to pay for a new one. B says the toy was all worn out, anyway.
   • Sibling A calls B a name and constantly teases. Child B retaliates by stealing or breaking property that belongs to A.
   • Siblings A and B are building with some blocks. They refuse to let younger sibling C help. Child C knocks down the tower.
   • Siblings A and B share a room. A makes a mess and doesn't clean up. B wants A to do a fair share of the clean up work.

5. **Student activity.** Have students read the story starter and then write an ending to the story. Suggest they think about how Jim, Jill, and Jane might solve their conflict. Have volunteers share their story endings. Do the endings promote a "win/win" solution? Or do they set up a situation that will lead to similar conflict in the future?

6. **Closure.** Summarize the main points of the lesson. Stress that recognizing the feelings of others, being willing to cooperate in looking for a solution, and talking together about the conflict can help open up ways to solve it.

● ●

Related Activities

- Extend the lesson to include classroom conflict resolution.

  Consider establishing a "peace table" in your classroom. (Many teachers who use conflict resolution in their classrooms find that it cuts down on time spent disciplining and gives them more time to teach. The children monitor themselves.) This does not have to be an actual table; it could be a mat or a pair of chairs. It is a designated spot where students can go when they are having some form of disagreement—a neutral location for working things out. Near the peace table, mount these directions:

1. Take turns talking and listening.
2. Brainstorm ideas.
3. Agree on a solution.

Stress the following important points. (1) If students can work through the formula cooperatively, the results are their own! They will be choosing what will happen in the future. (2) Sometimes they will have to repeat steps one and two several times before they can finish step three. (3) Sometimes it helps to begin (before step 1) by writing down what they think the problem is. After step 3 they may also write down what they have agreed upon and then both sign it. (The teacher may keep the contract.)

LESSON 4: FAMILY RULES

Preparation/Materials

- For student activity:
  poster board, one piece per student
  art materials of choice
- Optional: health puppets

Objectives

- Students will become aware of the purpose of family rules.
- Students will choose to honor family rules.

• •

Lesson

1. Tell the class about a rule in your family you didn't like very much. Ask students why they think your family had the rule and whether or not they think it was a good rule. Or if you and your class enjoy the health puppets, have Chris and Alex talk about a family rule (one puppet doesn't like the rule, but the other defends it).

2. Identify or elicit from students some reasons why families have rules for children:
   - for safety (calling parents from friends' homes to say where you are or when you're coming home, not using tools belonging to parents)
   - for health (going to bed at set times, eating properly, bathing frequently, limiting TV time)
   - for helping family members get along and sharing work in the home (doing chores, limiting telephone or bathroom time, sharing toys and games)

   Write the reasons on the board, and ask the class to give examples of each type of rule. Explain that even though children may not like all the rules in their family, the purpose of the rules is to keep them healthy and safe and to help them get along with others. Making rules is one way parents care for their children.

3. **Student activity**. Assign students to make posters illustrating a few of their family rules. Give students the opportunity to present and explain their posters to the rest of the class. Encourage them to identify why parents made the rule.

   Or try role reversal. Ask students to imagine that they are the parents and have them make up rules for the "children" in the home. Assign them to make a poster illustrating their rules. Discuss the posters and have class members explain the reasons for the rules.

4. **Closure:** "Today we talked about why families need some rules. Which rules are the hardest for you to follow?"

● ●

Related Activities

1. Enjoy Karla Kuskin's humorous poem "Rules" in the *Random House Book of Poetry for Children* (Random House, 1983). Students may also enjoy making up their own poems about rules.

2. Show the film *Families and Rules: Watch How Well Everything Works.* A 10-minute film showing how rules help a family live and work together.

LESSON 5: NEW BEGINNINGS— FORGIVENESS IN FAMILY LIFE

Preparation/Materials
- Write the poem "Up in the Pine" on chart paper.
- Songs of choice on lesson theme

Objectives
- Students will understand that God enables us to make new beginnings in family life.
- Students will learn or review the fifth commandment.

Background
Because family life has not escaped the effects of sin, relationships in families are marred by quarreling, estrangements, and lovelessness. The previous lessons on resolving family conflicts recognize that Christian families are not exempt from the alienating effects of sin. This lesson stresses that in Christ Christian families can find healing for broken relationships, forgiveness, and power to make new beginnings. By relying on God's grace and asking for the Spirit's power, family members can restore relationships and family life can be a source of joy.

As you teach this lesson, be sensitive to child abuse issues. Although children are called to obey and respect parents, parents are called to act in a Christ-like way and to respect children entrusted to their care as God's image-bearers.

- -

Lesson
1. Display the chart and read the following poem by Nancy Dingman Watson:

> **Up in the Pine**
> I'm by myself
> I want to be
> I don't want anyone
> Playing with me
>
> I'm all alone
> In the top of the pine
> Daddy spanked me
> And I don't feel fine
>
> I can look way out
> On the woods and lakes
> I can hear the buzz
> That the chain saw makes
>
> And a woodpecker chopping
> In the crabapple tree
> With his red crest bobbing
> But he doesn't see me

If anybody hollers
I'll pretend I'm not there
I may miss dinner
But I don't care

The pine needles swish
And the wind whistles free
And up in the pine
Is only me

It's starting to rain
But the tree keeps me dry
We toss in the black clouds
The tree and I

Now Daddy's calling.
He never stays mad.
He probably feels awful
Because I'm sad.

I'll answer Daddy.
He's concerned about the weather.
I'll climb down and he'll take my hand
And we'll go in the house together.

Read the poem with the class. Then ask students to tell the "story" of the poem. How does the child in the tree feel? What about the father? Why? How do they feel at the end of the poem?

2. **Discussion.** Use the poem as a springboard for talking about new beginnings in family life. Explain that because our families are part of the wider family of God what the Bible teaches about how we should live bears on our family life. Include the following points in discussion:

   - Teach or review God's commandment to honor father and mother. Discuss what it means. Note that God gave us this command (or rule) to help us in family life. Have students identify how it affects family life.

   - We all do and say hurtful things. Knowing about God's forgiveness and being able to ask God's help to say we're sorry makes a big difference in family life. We can make a new beginning.

   - Talk about why it's hard to say we're sorry. Have students suggest specific ways to communicate that they're sorry for what they did or said ("I'm sorry I hurt your feelings." "I was tired and crabby yesterday. I'm sorry I was mean." "I lost my temper; I'm sorry.") How do they feel after they tell someone they're sorry and how to they feel after someone apologizes to them?

3. Close the lesson by singing "Forgive Me, God, for Things I Do." Talk about the naming of the lyrics. If you wish, sing other songs of the theme of the lesson. Two suggestions are "Love, Love, Love" (*Proclaim 2,* 27) and "We Pray for Each Other" (*Songs of God's Love,* 69—verses 1 and 3).

• •

Related Activities

1. Have the class memorize and/or illustrate the poem "Up in the Pine." Or consider acting out the poem. Designate one desk or table as the tree and have a child sit on it. Then have others add sound effects (wind blowing, someone calling, woodpecker pecking, saw buzzing). Then have another child act the part of the father who calls and then meets the child climbing out of the "tree."

2. Read children's literature dealing with family relationships. Tape record one of the books and place it at a center for students to listen to. Have them write several sentences in response in their journals. Some titles:

Even If I Did Something Awful? by Barbara Hazen (emphasizes the unconditional love of parents)

Sisters by David McPhail

The Berenstain Bears Get in a Fight by Stan and Jan Berenstain

Thump and Plunk by Janice Udry

If It Weren't for You and *Timothy Too* by Charlotte Zolotow

Sometimes Papa and Mama Fight and *My Mother Never Listens to Me* by Marjorie Sharmat

Love You Forever by Robert Munsch

Forgive me, God, for things I do

Elizabeth McE. Shields, St. 1;
Sandra Myhr Anderson, St. 2;
Beverly Schultz Mullins, St. 3

John Day's Psalter

For - give me, God for things I do that are not kind and
I thank you, God, for Christ, your Son, who gave his life for
When some-one is un - kind to me then help me, God, to

good; for - give me, God, and help me try to
me that I might have for - give - ness now and
see how I can keep on lov - ing him as

do the things I should.
from my sin be free.
you keep lov - ing me.

LESSON 6: CELEBRATING FAMILY HERITAGE

Preparation/Materials

- Ask each student to bring an object from home that tells something about his or her heritage. Choose a heritage object of your own to show the class.
- Set up a display table for heritage objects. Cover it with colored paper or a cloth. Create various heights with boxes under the cloth or paper. Construct a large sign "Our Family Heritage" for the table.

- Mural paper
- Large talking balloon shape, one per student

Objectives

- Students will become aware of and appreciate their family heritage.
- Students will develop appreciation for diverse family styles and backgrounds.

Lesson

1. Introduce the lesson showing the class your family heritage object. Tell students what it means to your family or what it tells about your family background. Explain what the word *heritage* means. What things might be part of a family heritage?

2. Give each student the opportunity to present a heritage item and explain what it tells about his or her family. After presentations, students can put the objects on the display table.

3. **Circle talk.** Discuss the just-completed activity. Talk about variations and/or similarities in the family heritages that are represented. Make the point that families have different backgrounds and different styles of living and doing things. Encourage appreciation and acceptance of divergent family lifestyles.

   Note that each family has its own way of celebrating birthdays, baptisms, holidays or church feast days, or special family events (reunions, graduations, etc.). Have volunteers share some of their family traditions. Teach the word *traditions* to the class.

4. **Student activity.** Create a mural entitled "Our Family Traditions." Have each student illustrate a family tradition on a section of mural paper. Then give each child a large talking balloon on which to write a statement explaining or naming the tradition.

   Examples:

   I love baking Christmas cookies with Grandma.

   Every Sunday morning we eat pancakes.

   We watch fireworks on July 4.

   My family always goes to the woods to cut a Christmas tree.

61

Alternate options: each student can draw a self-portrait on the mural and then attach the talking balloon near the portrait. Or have students make only the talking balloons, and hang the balloons around the room or create a Family Traditions bulletin board with them.

5. **Closure.** Reflect on the lesson with students. Ask what they liked best about it. Or encourage them to look to the future: Are there any traditions they would like their family to start?

Related Activities

1. Have students write a few sentences on a 3" x 5" index card about their family heritage object. Attach the card to the object on the display table.

2. Invite parents, grandparents, and other classes to visit the classroom and enjoy the mural and display of items.

3. Ask one or more parents to talk to the class about their heritage and/or family traditions. If possible, invite parents from divergent cultural backgrounds.

4. Integrate with social studies and study family life in other cultures. What kind of family traditions or customs or holidays do they have? What are usual roles of family members?

5. Show pictures of family groupings from other cultures. Which family would each child like to visit? What do they think they might enjoy learning about that family? Have them write a few sentences (possibly in their journals) telling their choice of family and what they would like to know.

6. Focus on family stories—"Remember when Aunt Sue got stuck in the chair?" Find ways for students to share stories of funny events. For example, they can record the stories at a center for the whole class to enjoy.

LESSON 7: ME AND MY FAMILY GAME

Preparation/Materials

*   For student game:
    Student Activity
    file folders, one for each student
    dice or spinners, one die or spinner for each
        pair of students
    tokens or other playing pieces, one for each
        student
    art materials for decorating game boards
    blank game cards of construction paper of
        two contrasting colors, 10 of one color
        and 8 of the other for each student
        (Make colors light enough so writing
        will show.)
*   Make a sample game board to show the
    class.

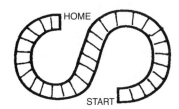

*   Write a note to parents to explain the board
    game. Suggest that parents play the game
    with their child and discuss the positive and
    negative squares.

Objectives

*   Students will make a game to review ups
    and downs of family life.
*   Students will identify some of their own ups
    and downs.

Lesson

1. Introduce the lesson project—making a Me and My Family game. Explain that students
    will make gameboards on which they will write events from their own life. Show stu-
    dents the sample game board.

2. Making the game—step 1. Work with students to help them list what they will write on
    their personal game squares. They should write personal events in about 10 squares.
    Suggest they identify 6 positive or "good" things that happened to them (or family
    members) and about 4 negative or "bad" things.

    Turn to the Student Activity in the student workbook. Walk students through the process
    of choosing events to use in their games. (This functions as a review as you recall con-
    cepts covered in the unit.) Have students write down their rough ideas on the top part of
    the worksheet. Suggest or elicit from students a few "good" or "bad" things to spark
    ideas, but have students write down something from their own family life experience.

    Suggested review format:
    *   God planned for us to live in families. Our families love and care for us in many
        ways. Ask students to recall ways. Suggest or elicit a few "good" things to write down.
        Examples:
            Adopted/born into my family. God gave me a family.
            My warm bed.
            Family takes care of me.

- God has planned us to be boys and girls.
  Examples:
    I like being a girl/boy.
    I can do …
    I want to be …
    I'm good at …
- Family members sometimes fight or hurt each other's feelings.
  Examples:
    Fight about TV.
    Tease my brother.
- We need rules for families to run smoothly and for our own protection. (Ask students to think of a rule they kept or perhaps broke.)
  Examples:
    Cleaned up my room.
    Forgot to feed the dog.
- We have a family heritage and family traditions.
  Examples:
    Made cookies with …
    Went camping with …
    Ate pumpkin pie at …

Other ideas to include are personal events such as catching the measles, breaking an arm or leg, having tonsils removed, making room for a new brother or sister, moving, or a special vacation trip. Consider having students end with a positive, affirming square ("I'm 8 and feeling great", or "I'm a big 7 now").

3. Making the game—step 2. Next, students should sort out their suggestions and decide which they will use on the game board. (Note that they'll need to use as few words as possible.) Direct them to write their final choices in chronological order in the space provided on the bottom of the worksheet. You may wish to check the list at this stage.

Have students write playing instructions on 10 bonus or plus cards of one color and 8 minus cards of another color. Brainstorm a list of instruction suggestions and write them on the board.
    Examples:
      Miss one turn.
      Take another turn.
      Go back one space.
      Go ahead two spaces.
      Move to the next (color) square.

Again, they can write their choices on the worksheet. Have them fill in the name of the correct color on the bottom of the worksheet. Then have them write their choices on the construction paper cards of the correct color.

4. Making the game—step 3. Each student makes a game board on the inside of a file folder. Show students the sample. Demonstrate how to draw a game path ("a snake with two curves"). Direct them to draw it very lightly in pencil first on the folder and to check with you before going over the lines with markers.

   Next, students mark off approximately 30 spaces. Have them write out the ten personal events from their worksheet on ten of the board spaces. Have them color code the personal squares to the game cards (positive squares one color and negative squares another).

5. Making the game—step 4. Students can decorate their game boards and, if time permits, the outside of the file folder (a design incorporating names of family members might be suggested).

6. Playing the game. Explain how to play. You may wish to write out the instructions and give students a copy.
   How to play:
   - Two players for each game board (Students can play with a partner. After one round use the partner's game board.)
   - One die or spinner
   - One token or playing piece for each player
   - Place the game cards of each color in a separate pile. Place them face down on the game board.
   - Roll a die or spin the spinner. Move the right number of spaces.
   - When landing on a colored/personal space, take a card of the same color. Follow the directions. Return the card face down to the bottom of the pile.
   - The first player to reach HOME wins.

   Give students time to enjoy playing their games.

7. **Closure.** Talk about the activity. What was the hardest about making the games? What was the most fun? Tell students that the game is theirs to take home and play with family members. Put a note to parents in each file folder.

LESSON 8: DEALING WITH DEATH

Preparation/Materials
- Books of choice for Options 2 and 3

Objectives
- Students will recognize that all human beings must die as a result of sin.
- Students will recognize that in the face of death sadness is a fitting emotion.
- Students will know the comfort of the Christian hope.

Background

The tendency of many North American adults is to try to shield children from the reality of death. The motivation is a desire to protect children, to make the children's lives easier. But death is an inescapable part of life—even for children—in a world marred by sin. Trying to screen out death actually does children a disservice. In fact, with no guidance from parents or teachers, children may struggle with distorted ideas or fears. By guiding their learning about death, adults give children correct information and open the possibility of sharing feelings and fears about death. In the Christian community, they can convey the hope of resurrection life in Christ.

Ruth Kopp in a helpful book entitled *Where Has Grandpa Gone?* helps us understand the concept of death a child has at various age levels. Between the ages of two and six, most children see "everything that moves and has activity as being alive and personal." Since young children also tend to personify abstract ideas, as they become aware of death they think of it as a powerful being that can "come at will and remove people and pets" they love. They develop a variety of ways to fend off the "monster death." Children from about three and four years old, for example, may hide in the comfort of a security blanket, while from about four to six or seven, they use "fantasy, magic, and wishful thinking" to protect themselves and those they love. But gradually at about six or seven, children acquire what Kopp calls a materialist attitude toward death: they shift their protection against death "from fantasy to the tangible, physical world." In this phase they become aware of their bodies and how they work and find a defense against death in physical fitness—an idea reinforced by North American society. They think that if they are strong and healthy enough, they can prevent illness or injury. During the next phase from about eight to eleven, children rationally explore their world and the idea of death. They look for reasons and explanations for illnesses, for the most part ignoring the emotions.

So from a young age children are aware of death, and they struggle to deal with it. It isn't possible to shield them from death. However, by sensitively dealing with the subject, we can offer them support and hold out to them the comfort of being a child of God and trusting God to make all things well.

In teaching about death and dying, we should also be aware of the mistaken and unbiblical emphasis in much of the current literature on the topic. Death is often presented as the natural end of life. We are urged to accept death as a natural and, sometimes, even as a beautiful and fitting end to life. It's true, of course, that in the world as we know it—a broken world suffering under the effects of sin—death is a fact and the life cycle inevitably ends in death. But the Bible clearly teaches that death is not a friend but an enemy. Death is the result of human sin. God created us not for death but for life. Christians believe Christ has removed the sting of death and in him we already have new life that never ends. Christ's resurrection body is the guarantee of the resurrection of our bodies.

This lesson—included in *Horizons Health* at kindergarten, grade 1, and grade 2—provides several activities and lists of resources from which to choose. Your choices will depend on what approach you are comfortable with and on your classroom situation. We suggest you use the resources for a session on the subject of death at the close of this unit on the family and/or when the subject of death comes up naturally in the classroom or fits in with the class's

Bible studies (for example, tie it in with the lesson on the death of Elijah or with your celebration of Easter). Since there is not much children's literature on death written from a Christian perspective, bear in mind that it is crucial to critically read the books listed below and to provide Christian perspective through comment and discussion.

• •

Lesson

Option 1. Tell about the loss of someone you know, how sad you felt and how you missed the person. Talk about the source of your comfort and how that helped you.

Option 2. Introduce the idea of change or loss by reading a book about moving and loss entailed by the ones who are moving or staying. Use this as a starting point for discussing loss through death.

We Are Best Friends by Aliki

My Friend William Moved Away by Martha Hickman

Ira Says Goodbye by Bernard Waber

Janey by Charlotte Zolotow

Mitchell Is Moving by Marjorie Sharmat

Moving Molly by Shirley Hughes

Option 3. Use the subject of the death of pets to lead into a general discussion of death. Tell students about a pet you or one of your family members had that died and read one of the many excellent books available on the death of a pet. Although these books focus on the death of pets, many of them obliquely refer to death of people. Some available book titles:

Father's Laika by Mats Wahl

Jim's Dog Muffins by Miriam Cohen

Goodbye, Max by Holly Keller

The Dead Bird by Margaret Wise Brown

Better With Two by Catherine Stock

It Must Hurt a Lot: A Child's Book About Death by Doris Sanford

After reading the story, have students identify some of the feelings that the main character or characters had. Allow time for students to ask questions or to talk about family pets that have died. Stress that sadness is an appropriate feeling when a loved pet dies.

Option 4. Read a book dealing with human death. Although these books deal with death in a sensitive way, none of them is written from a Christian perspective. Thus it is important to read the books critically and spend time discussing the Christian hope in the face of death.

Goodbye Rune by Marit Kaldhol and Wenche Oyen

My Grandma Leonie by Bijou LeTord

Grandpa's Slide Show by Deborah Gould

The Saddest Time by Norma Simon

Marianne's Grandmother by Bettina Egger

I Had a Friend Named Peter: Talking to Children About Death

Nana Upstairs, Nana Downstairs by Tomie de Paola

Everett Anderson's Goodbye by Lucille Clifton

One book with a solid Christian perspective, *Emma Says Goodbye* by Carolyn Nystrom, deals with the death of a child's aunt from leukemia. Although the book is too difficult for most grade 2 students, teachers may wish to read parts of it or use ideas for discussion.

Option 5. Use an occasion that naturally arises in the classroom, the death of a relative or friend of a class member, to talk about the subject of death. Be sure to stress the Christian hope, but also talk about feelings connected with death. Although Christians believe in new and eternal life in Christ, grief is nonetheless a fitting response to the loss of a loved one. Identify concrete ways to help the one who is grieving.

Use appropriate Scripture passages such as Psalm 23 or the story of Jesus' resurrection as a basis for continued discussion. And sing appropriate songs about Christ's resurrection or about the comfort of the Christian hope. A few suggested titles:

"Children of the Heavenly Father" (*Psalter Hymnal,* 440; *Songs of God's Love,* 62)

"He's Got the Whole World in His Hands" (*Songs of God's Love,* 56)

"The Lord's My Shepherd" (*Proclaim Songbook 2,* 16; *Psalter Hymnal,* 161; alternate tune, *Children's Hymnbook,* 19)

"Christ the Lord Is Risen Today" (*Proclaim Songbook 2,* 25)

Unit 3

Getting Along with Others

Goals

- Students will develop a Christian perspective on relationships with others.
- Students will develop skills for getting along with others.

Background

Christians recognize the power of sin to break down communication, mar relationships, and disrupt community. But Christians believe that the risen Christ has power to transform and renew us and our relationship to God and also to others. In this context "getting along with others" means much more than learning a set of skills (although interpersonal skills are important) or following a set of specific behavior patterns.

The apostle Paul addresses the problem of interpersonal relationships in these words: "But the fruit of the Spirit is love, joy, peace, patience, kindness, goodness, faithfulness, gentleness and self-control…. Since we live by the Spirit, let us keep in step with the Spirit. Let us not become conceited, provoking and envying each other" (Galatians 5: 22, 25, 26). Keeping in step with the Spirit will lead us away from self-centeredness—and toward the self-control and concern for others necessary for living in community.

This unit, then, is not a Dale Carnegie mini-course. The lessons are not meant to promote a self-serving "you scratch my back and I'll scratch yours" outlook. Rather, by giving students the opportunity to show courtesy, kindness, and love to others and to learn about getting along with others, we are nurturing them in the life of the Spirit.

Vocabulary

Integrate the following suggested vocabulary:

manners	appreciation	listen	selfish/unselfish
please	thank you	excuse me	communication
generous	sorry	cooperate	you're welcome

Unit Resources

Getting Along. San Francisco: Children's Television Resource and Education Center, 1988.
> *Getting Along* is a 63-page book with a 60-minute song and story cassette. Its stories, songs, and activities were created "to help kids work and play together." Order from the publisher at 330 Townsend St., San Francisco, California 94107.

Gibbs, Jeanne. *Tribes: A Process for Social Development and Cooperative Learning.* Santa Rosa, Calif.: Center Source Publications, 1987.
> Although the scope of this book is much broader than the content of this unit, its suggestions for cooperative activities make it a helpful teacher resource. Order from the publisher: 305 Tesconi Circle, Santa Rosa, California 95401.

Hill, Susan and Tim. *The Collaborative Classroom: A Guide to Co-operative Learning.* Portsmouth, N.H.: Heinemann, 1990.
> This book is "about people learning and working together, rather than alone." A valuable resource, not only for unit activities but also for establishing a truly cooperative classroom.

Hiller, Ron. *Ronno's "Getting Along" Theme Pack.* Kitchener, Ont.: Song Support, 1991.
Includes "Let's Co-operate" and The Good Manners Song," two original songs tying in with the unit theme. In the pack are a 38-page booklet with the piano/vocal score and an audio-cassette. Order from the publisher: Station C, Box 722, Kitchener, Ontario, Canada N2G 4B6 or Suite 162, 255 Grant Arrow Ave., Buffalo, New York 14207-3081.

Prutzman, Priscilla, and others. *Friendly Classroom for a Small Planet.* Philadelphia: New Society Publishers, 1988.
Children's Creative Response to Conflict, an organization with Quaker roots, developed this resource. It contains suggestions and activities for building community, learning to communicate, and promoting self-awareness and empathy. Available from the publisher: P.O. Box 582, Santa Cruz, California 95061.

Lesson Resources

Lesson 2

Aliki. *Manners.* New York: Greenwillow, 1990.
Amusing illustrations and a handwritten text combine for a delightful look at manners.

Berry, Joy W. *What to Do When Your Mom or Dad Says … "What Should You Say Dear?"* Chicago: Children's Press.

Brown, Marc, and Stephen Krensky. *Perfect Pigs: An Introduction to Manners.* New York: Atlantic Monthly Press, 1983.

Dellinger, Annetta E. *Good Manners for God's Children.* St. Louis: Concordia, 1984.

Good Manners. Teaching Picture Set. Marvel.

The pictures of this set are 10" x 13" and are accompanied by a teacher manual. Available at teacher stores or order from the publisher at Suite 1303, 212 Fifth Ave., New York, New York 10010.

Hartley, Hermine. *The Family Book of Manners.* Westwood, N.J.: Barbour, 1990.

Hoban, Russell. *Dinner at Alberta's.* New York: Harper: 1975.
Because Arthur the crocodile eats like a beast, his family is trying to shape up his manners for dinner at Alberta's. A read-along audiocassette available from KIMBO, Dept. 8, P.O. Box 447, Long Branch, New Jersey 07740-0477; phone 800-631-2187.

Leaf, Munro. *Manners Can Be Fun.* 3rd ed. New York: Harper Junior Books, 1985.

Moncure, Jane. *Excuse Me.* Chicago: Children's Press, 1989.

Simon, Norma. *What Do I Say?* Niles, Ill.: Whitman, 1983.

Stouse, Karla F.. *Act Nicely, Please.* St. Meinrad, Ind.: Abbey, 1987.

Lesson 5

Micallef, Mary. *Listening: The Basic Connection.* Carthage, Ill.: Good Apple, 1984.
Contains reproducible activities that cover listening awareness, motivation, and related topics. Although the activities are intended for grades 3-8, many ideas can be adapted for lower grades.

LESSON 1: COMMUNICATING

Preparation/Materials

- For making student postboxes:
  manila envelope or piece of construction
  paper, one per student; or white paper
  plate, 1 1/2 per student
  art materials for decorating
  stapler
- Slips of paper on which are written names
  of class members
- Song about loving one another

Objectives

- Students will express appreciation of others.
- Students will become aware of the importance of showing love to others.
- Students will consider the meaning of loving their neighbor.

Lesson

1. Introduce the unit by writing the unit title, "Getting Along With Others," on the board. Tell students they will be talking and learning about ways to get along with others. Note that this lesson is about communication. Recall the importance of communication in family life. Tell the class that this unit is about getting along with people in the wider community—with neighbors, friends, and school community. Explain that communication is important in getting along with others at school and in the classroom, too.

2. Ask students to help you set up a class communication center, a place where they can send each other messages. Have the children make and decorate their own "postboxes" for the center. Use manila envelopes, construction paper (fold up bottom third of the sheet and staple the sides together), or paper plates (cut a paper plate in half; staple one half to a whole paper plate—front to front). Hang the postboxes on the wall where students can easily reach them. Be sure to hang one with your own name on it. Throughout the unit use the message center to encourage students in positive communication—to thank someone for sharing or for helping them, to give compliments, to apologize, or to cheer someone up.

3. Give students the opportunity to use the communication center right away. Provide each student with a slip of paper bearing the name of a class member. Direct students to write and post a friendly note to "their student." Suggest that students give an honest compliment ("I like the way you ..." or "I'm glad I know you because ...").

4. **Discussion.** Talk about the warm and good feelings that the notes generated—for both the sender and the receiver. End the discussion by reviewing Jesus' command to love our neighbors as ourselves.

5. **Closure.** Sing an appropriate song such as "Love One Another" (*Songs of God's Love,* 64) or verse one of "Love God With All Your Soul" (*Children's Hymnbook,* 169) or "Love, Love, Love, Love" (*Songs of God's Love,* 27). Teach the class John 13:34b: "Love one another. As I have loved you, so you must love one another."

· ·

Related Activities

- To sustain interest in the communication center, write one-sentence notes to the children and "deliver" them before the next school day starts. Give a bright start to the day by having them read the notes.

Consider asking other school staff members to use the center to communicate with the class during this unit (after the Lesson 3 project would be an appropriate time).

LESSON 2: MANNERS MAKE A DIFFERENCE

Preparation/Materials

- Health puppets
- Drawing paper, one sheet per student
- Optional: *Manners* by Aliki
- Optional: student puppets from Unit 1, Lesson 3

Objectives

- Students will reflect on the purpose of good manners.
- Students will identify socially acceptable ways of acting in specific situations.
- Students will practice using good manners.

Background

Showing courtesy is one way of loving our neighbors. Waiting our turn in line, thanking someone for a favor or for help, and excusing ourselves when we reach or step in front of someone are all ways of demonstrating our concern for others. Courtesy takes the other person's feelings and needs into account and recognizes the contribution or help of others. As you teach this lesson, stress that basic courtesy is treating others the same way you would like to be treated.

But there is another side to courtesy. Every society has a set of rules that govern social situations. Knowing these rules and feeling comfortable with them will help children feel at ease socially, promoting self-confidence.

Lesson

1. Use the puppets Chris and Alex to act out situations modeling good manners. First act out bad manners and get reactions from the class. Then reenact the scene showing good manners. Consider covering the following topics:
   - manners and "magic words" (*please, thank you, you're welcome, excuse me, sorry*)
   - greeting manners (use the person's name and, if appropriate, title—"Hello, Mr. Smith")
   - school assembly/chapel manners (listening, not distracting others, etc.)
   - conversation manners (listening to and looking at the speaker, taking turns talking)
   - eating manners (sitting straight, chewing with closed mouth, not stuffing mouth, asking for food instead of reaching, not burping)
   - manners and introductions (when being introduced to adults, stand, shake any hand offered, say a friendly hello)

   A good resource for this step is Aliki's book *Manners*. The "let's pretend" sequences can easily be adapted to puppet scripts.

   Alternate option: read a book with the class about manners. Suggested titles:
   What Do You Do When Your Mom or Dad Says … "What Should You Say, Dear?" by Joy Berry
   Good Manners for God's Children by Annetta Dellinger
   Perfect Pigs by Marc Brown and Stephen Krensky

2. Give students the opportunity to practice using good manners. Have them roleplay or use their puppets to act out social situations. Divide the class into groups and assign each group a situation to act out.
   - birthday party—one person is receiving and opening gifts
   - eating refreshments at a party
   - casual meeting in school hall of two students and one or two teachers
   - asking for a special favor (for example, using someone's bike or game) and then returning the item or saying thanks
   - being introduced to friends of parents
   - telephone conversations

3. Have class members identify one aspect of good manners that they have trouble with and write a sentence or two describing their problem ("When I meet teachers in the hall, I feel shy and want to look at the floor" or "When I see the birthday cake, it looks so good that I start eating and forget to say thank you"). Then have them draw an illustration of themselves overcoming the problem or following good manners. They can put word balloons into the pictures. Ask volunteers to share their trouble spots. This could be a center activity.

4. **Closure.** Reflect on the lesson with questions such as the following: "Do you think manners are important? Why or why not? How do you feel when someone steps on your toe and doesn't say excuse me? (Or use some other typical classroom situation.) How are feelings and manners connected?"

Related Activities

1. Integrate with language arts. For example, read and write poetry about manners. "Table Manners" by Gelett Burgess is about the Goops who have terrible table manners. Or read *Dinner at Alberta's* by Russell Hoban and write a class story about trying to shape up someone's manners.

2. Integrate with social studies and learn about manners in other countries you are studying. Or invite a member of the community to talk to the class about manners in another culture. What are considered good manners and bad manners in the culture? How do people show appreciation or make introductions?

3. Tie in the lesson with giving thanks to God. Tell the story of Jesus and the healing of the ten lepers (Luke 17:11-19).

4. Play a circle game about manners. Stand in a circle. Start the game by turning to the person next to you and saying, "Hi, my name is…." The next person does the same thing, and the introductions pass around the circle. On succeeding rounds add some variety—pass a handshake, speed up or reverse directions, or add a greeting in a foreign language.

LESSON 3: SHOWING APPRECIATION

Preparation/Materials
- Paper for letter-writing activity, class supply
- Art materials for student pictures
- Optional: chart paper

Objectives
- Students will identify those in the community who help them.
- Students will express appreciation to school helpers.

Lesson

1. Ask children to name people in the school community who help them each day and identify how each one helps. Make a list of the names on the board or on a chart (persons to include: office staff, custodian, bus drivers, other teachers, teacher aides, librarian, school nurse, volunteer parent helpers, principal, or students in other classes).

2. Suggest that the class express appreciation to some or all of these people by writing letters and drawing pictures for them. Have each student write to one person on the list. The letter can begin "Thank you for ..." and then specify the help the person has given. Another option is to work together to compose a class letter for students to copy. The pictures can depict the helpful service.

   If possible, groups of students should hand deliver their letters and pictures. This will give them the opportunity to see how delighted the recipients are. Have class members share these experiences.

3. **Closure.** Reflect on the lesson with the class with questions similar to the following:
   - "How does it make you feel when you tell someone thank you or to tell someone you appreciate them? Why do you think you feel that way?"
   - "How do you feel when someone tells you they appreciate what you've done?"

Related Activities

1. Plan follow-up activities to help build relationships between class members and school personnel. Have the class make birthday or holiday greeting cards or invite one or more of the school staff to a class celebration or some other class event.

2. Have students use the communication center to show appreciation to each other. Take care that every student receives a note of appreciation.

LESSON 4: HELPING EACH OTHER

Preparation/Materials

- For making a helping tree:
  a large, dried tree branch
  container filled with sand for "planting" the
    tree (optional: use plaster of Paris
    instead of sand)
  fruit or flower shapes made of construction
    paper
  hole punch
  yarn or string

- Optional: a health puppet

Objectives

- Students will recognize times when they can help others or when they may appreciate having help.
- Students will practice communicating to others their willingness to help.

• •

Lesson

1. Act out a situation in which you need some help—perhaps to carry items or to reach something when your arms are full. Or interact with one of the health puppets and present a similar situation ("Alex, what's the problem? You're huffing and puffing! Is that package heavy?")

2. Ask students to describe the situation just acted out and then to tell about similar situations they have encountered. Talk about the relief when someone reaches out a helpful hand. And point out, too, that sometimes we can help each other avoid accidents or dangerous situations (warning someone who doesn't notice a ball whizzing in his or her direction or who doesn't hear an approaching car). Emphasize the importance of showing love for neighbors in the "small" things of life.

3. Sing the following song to the tune of "She'll Be Coming Round the Mountain" as a lighthearted way to reinforce the lesson concept:

   > We can all help each other, yes we can.
   > We can all help each other, yes we can.
   > When we're in a bit of trouble,
   > We can count on one another.
   > We can all help each other, yes we can.

   Sing it through several times and have students clap or stamp their feet twice after the first, second, and last lines.

   Another suggestion: Teach students the song by Willard Jabusch based on Matthew 25:35, 36, 40, "Whatsoever You Do to the Least" (*Psalter Hymnal,* 210). Discuss the lyrics with the class. How do we do the things mentioned in the song for Christ when we do them for others?

4. Have students use the communication center to write messages offering help to others if they are ever in a "bit of trouble." Again, make sure that all send and receive communications.

5. Follow-up by highlighting helpful acts. "Plant" a tree branch in a sand-filled container and label it "The Helping Tree." Have each recipient of a helpful act write one sentence describing it ("John helped me get my boot off") on a leaf, flower, or fruit shape and hang it on the tree.

6. Close the lesson by summarizing main concepts and encouraging students to continue to contribute to the helping tree.

• •

Related Activities

1. Involve the students in a class or school project to do something to help others at school or in the community. (Have volunteers sign up to do litter patrol on the playground once a week; collect food, clothes, used books, or pennies for a helping community program; sing for residents of a nursing home; set up a bird feeding station and take turns tending it.)

2. Students can use their puppets to act out ways to help each other and others at school or in the community. Although having a helping project is a better learning experience, interacting with puppets and each other can raise student awareness and give new insights.

LESSON 5: FRIENDLY LISTENING

Preparation/Materials
- An object to hide
- For student activity
  Student Activity
  optional: hole punch and pieces of yarn or
  string for hanging circles 1 and 2
  art materials for coloring or decorating
  awards

Objectives
- Students will identify characteristics of active listening.
- Students will become aware of the importance of active listening.
- Students will practice listening skills.

Background
"Listening is a skill that can be learned and an art that can be mastered.... We owe it to ourselves to make it our best language art!" This quotation from a popular book on teaching listening to children turns the purpose of listening on its head. Listening is not something we owe to ourselves. Listening to others is one way of loving them. Active listening means that we are receptive to others, that we value them and their ideas. This lesson tries to make students aware of what's involved in listening and why listening is important. It helps them practice and improve their listening skills. But keep the emphasis of the lesson straight, for although paying attention to skills can make us conscious of what's going on in the communication process and help us express ourselves more clearly, skills are no substitute for sincere interest and concern.

Lesson (2 sessions)

1. Begin with an activity that will help the class practice listening and will focus their attention. Direct students to put their heads on their desks or tables, close their eyes, and listen to classroom sounds. To add interest, move your desk chair, close a desk drawer or a book, or use the stapler or pencil sharpener. After a short time, ask class members to share what they heard. Consider doing the activity a second time and have the class to listen to sounds outside the classroom.

2. Next, do one of the following activities:
   - Ask one child to leave the room. Then hide an object such as a box of crayons somewhere in the classroom. The child comes back into the room and tries to find the object. The rest of the class signals how "hot" or "cold" the child is by humming or clapping. They hum louder as the child approaches the object and more softly as he or she moves away. Don't explain the humming or clapping to the one trying to find the object.

     Gather students into a circle and talk about how they communicated in the activity. Did the child who was looking for the object catch on right away to what the noise meant? Why or why not?

- Play the Telephone Game. Have class members sit in a circle. Start a whispered message, which the children pass around the circle. Most likely by the time the message has reached the last person, it will be garbled. Identify why it changed. Ask: "What helps you to hear a message correctly?" Lead students to identify specific things that might help the communication (for example, speaking clearly, speaking slowly, speaking close to ear, no other distracting noises). Write the suggestions on the board. Then try passing another message around the circle. Make the sentence difficult enough so that students must listen carefully. Check on the results. If the message still didn't get through, send a third message around the circle. This time allow listeners who are unsure of the message, to check with speakers and find out whether or not they heard correctly (listener: "I heard you say …"; speaker "No, I said … " or "Yes").

3. **Discussion.** Talk about listening and its importance. Tell a personal anecdote about a time when you were telling a person something and then you realized the person wasn't really listening. Students may have anecdotes of their own to tell. Ask students how they felt when others didn't listen to them.

   Elicit anecdotes about times when class members had good listeners. Identify characteristics of active listening: paying attention, looking at the speaker, and responding in various ways (nodding head, smiling or showing in other ways that one is involved in the conversation, asking questions or making remarks). Review the listening procedure taught in grade 1: Stop what you're doing, look at the speaker, listen to what the speaker is saying.

   Ask: "Why do we like others to listen to us: (Include these reasons in the answer: it shows interest in us and shows that others care about us.) "Why do you think we should listen to others?"

4. **Student activity.** The award on the activity sheet provides class members with positive reinforcement. Tell students you are awarding these to everyone for practicing good listening. Students can cut out the award and write their names in the blank.

   Use the other materials on the page to promote listening awareness in the classroom. Ask students to color and cut them out. Direct them to complete circle 2 by writing in the words "Stop, look, and listen." Punch holes in circles 1 and 2 and hang them in strategic places around the room. Students can wear the listening buttons and award the "Thank you for listening" button to a family member who listens to them. Or consider collecting copies of the thank-you button and awarding the button to students when they exhibit good listening skills.

5. **Closure.** Ask students to summarize the lesson. What is active listening? Why are good listening skills important?

● ●

Related Activities

- Center idea: have groups of students record friendly conversations. Provide some conversation guidelines such as topic and length of conversation. Listen to the recordings for cues about class listening practices. Does one person talk much more of the time? How can you tell if someone isn't listening to the speaker?

LESSON 6: HEY! THAT'S MINE!

Preparation/Materials

- Make an audio recording of remarks that reflect both selfish and generous or cooperative attitudes. Put all the selfish remarks together at the beginning of the tape. Some suggested remarks:

  "Hey! That's mine."

  "Give it back!"

  "No, you can't have any."

  "Leave my ___ alone."

  "That's your problem."

  "Keep your hands off my stuff."

  "You can use ___ for a while."

  "May I have it back?"

  "Let's ___ together."

  "Do you want to trade?"

  "I want my ____ now, but later on you can use it again."

  "Let's trade."
- Tape recorder
- Write unselfish remarks on a set of large cards.
- Choose a sharing activity and plan for students to provide items accordingly (Step 2).

- Student Activity

Objectives

- Students will identify attitudes/remarks as selfish or unselfish.
- Students will practice sharing.

Background

Since egocentrism is a normal characteristic of early childhood, sharing is a very difficult concept for young children to grasp. Some think sharing means that others should give them what they want; some only see that they must give up something. Children begin to understand sharing by learning to take turns and to see how other children enjoy their turns. Gradually they come to understand the position and viewpoint of another person. Children around the age of 5 become less possessive about objects but more possessive about people. Sharing friends is may be very difficult for some students. Use this lesson to encourage them in the direction of sharing, of loving their neighbors.

Lesson

1. Play the tape recording of selfish statements. Introduce the recording by telling students that sometimes it's helpful to stop and listen to ourselves and hear what we sound like to others. Ask them to listen and see if they hear themselves.

   After listening to the recording, ask: "Did you hear yourself?" If no one admits making such remarks, admit that you heard yourself on the recording. Lead students in a discussion of common selfish attitudes that all struggle with.

   Then play the recording of generous statements. Compare these attitudes to the selfish attitudes. Talk about why it matters whether or not we are generous.

   Hang the cards with unselfish remarks on the classroom wall. Consider putting up one or two of the cards each day. Read all of the cards each day as you post new ones. Refer to the cards during the day to remind students who are having difficulty sharing.

Alternate option: Have the class brainstorm lists of selfish and unselfish statements. Write the lists on chart paper and display them in the room.

2. Have a sharing activity. Involve the class in an activity such as the following:
   - Share a treat. Have the class prepare a treat and then invite another class to share it. Ask the students to bring the ingredients and have them do the preparation. (Fruit kabobs, crackers and cheese, or raisin/nut mixtures with fruit juice are healthful, easy treats to prepare.)
   - Have a "Book Sharing Day." Each child brings a book from home (or a book chosen from the library if necessary). Students team up and "swap" books or take turns reading their book to their partner. After reading time, each student does a book review for the class on the book that his or her partner brought to share.

3. **Student activity.** Have students read the story starter and then write an ending to the story. To create interest, read the beginning of the story with the class. Depending on your classroom situation, you may also wish to discuss Tess and Zak's problem and have students identify one or more solutions as a prewriting activity. Or have groups discuss the problem and then have individuals write their own endings.

4. **Closure.** Summarize the lesson. Ask students what they liked best about the lesson and why.

● ●

Related Activities

1. Have students make up and produce skits on selfish/unselfish behavior. They can use puppets to act out the skits. Consider making this a center activity.

2. Write poems about sharing or about selfishness. Direct students to write the word *sharing* as the first line of the poem and then to write words or phrases that come to mind about sharing. (The words and phrases can be unrhymed.)

Examples:

Sharing	Selfish
Friendly	Mine, Mine!
Warm heart	Cold
A happy feeling	Uncaring
Makes enough for all	Pushes me away

Have volunteers share their poems. Or have students write or paste their poems on construction paper and add illustrations. Consider gathering the poems into a book to "share" with another class.

LESSON 7: COOPERATIVE VENTURES

Preparation/Materials

- Materials necessary for chosen activities in step 2
- Optional: Pictures of people cooperating (putting on a party, parade, play; building a house; taking part in sports or games)

Objectives

- Students will recognize the importance of cooperation.
- Students will develop cooperative skills.
- Students will choose to cooperate.

• •

Lesson

1. If you have collected pictures of people cooperating, briefly talk about each picture and identify how they are cooperating. Discuss ways class members cooperate and what would happen if they didn't cooperate.

2. Have the class engage in one or more cooperative activities. Suggestions:
    - Select two fairly well-matched students to arm wrestle for candy. Tell them that each time their opponent's hand touches the table they will receive a reward. They must not talk during the activity. The students' first instinct will probably be to struggle to overcome the opponent. Allow them to continue their wrestling for a while. If they don't come up with a better solution and silently communicate it to their partner, ask the class for any ideas on how they could both win more candy. (If each stops struggling and they take turns being submissive, they can quickly rack up many more rewards.) Encourage the contestants to share their rewards with the whole class.
    - Put the students' desks together in small groups. Assign each student a job (group janitor, group encourager, group mail deliverer, group leader). Attach a printed card to each person's desk naming his or her position. Rotate roles on a regular basis. In this way students help classmates and work together to develop a more orderly classroom.
    - Use a "finish the story" activity about cooperating. Assign pairs of students to work on it together. They must share ideas, cooperate to decide who will write it down and who will illustrate or if they will split up those responsibilities.
    - Turn your class into a newspaper staff to produce a class newspaper. Divide the students into groups. Assign each group a "section" for which they are responsible (sports, fashion, entertainment, school news, local news, travel, etc.). Each section needs reporters, illustrators, writers, printers (typist), and a layout editor. These jobs can be shared or cooperatively assigned.

3. **Closure:** "This lesson was about cooperating. Was cooperating hard or easy when you (name of activity)? Why was it necessary to cooperate to (name of activity)?"

4. **Unit review.** Recall that the unit title is "Getting Along With Others." Write the words on the board. Call out key unit words (*communicating, listening, manners, appreciation, unselfishness, cooperating*). Ask students to tell the word's connection with getting along with others. Or provide words that describe antisocial behavior and ask students to describe how these behaviors keep us from getting along with others. Possibly make this a group activity with groups brainstorming the effects of the negative behavior and what changes in behavior would lead to getting along with others.

Consider closing the unit by reciting John 13:34b together and singing an appropriate song.

Unit 4

Growth and Development

Goals

- Students will develop body awareness.
- Students will learn basics of eye and ear health and safety.
- Students will develop understanding of hearing and seeing impairments and empathy for those with impairments.
- Students will choose to take responsibility for taking care of their eyes and ears.

Background

In *Beyond Doubt* (Christian Reformed Board of Publications, 1980) Cornelius Plantinga tells an anecdote about Whittaker Chambers, a dedicated atheist. One day when Chambers was watching his child as she sat in her high chair, "he found himself staring with fascination at his daughter's tiny, intricate ear. It seemed to him a marvel. Only a *planner* could have planned that ear." This experience "set Chambers on the road to belief."

The human body is truly amazing. And it's very smart. In fact, it's brilliant. It performs to a large extent "on its own." The heart beats, lungs breathe, stomach digests, kidneys purify—all without our even thinking about it. When we study the human body—its parts, processes, growth, and development, we cannot help but wonder at the complexity of its design. But our study should lead us to marvel not only at the body, but at the God who created it.

God has given us life, and that life is mysteriously and inextricably linked to a body so complex that we will never completely understand it. Our fitting response is awe and wonder and praise to God, the Creator. "I will praise you," said the psalmist, "because I am fearfully and wonderfully made; your works are wonderful, I know that full well" (Psalm 139:14).

Vocabulary

Integrate the following suggested vocabulary:

			parts of the eye:	*parts of the ear:*
height	vision	senses	eyebrow	pinna
measurement	glasses	hearing aid	eyelashes	eardrum
body system	tear	blood	upper eyelid	outer ear
bone	blink	noise/noisy	pupil	middle ear
skeleton	protect	system	sclera	inner ear
muscles	braille		iris	hammer
breathing	hearing		lower eyelid	anvil
				stirrup

Unit Resources

Contact local branches of national organizations that deal with issues related to blindness and deafness for educational materials.

Lesson Resources

Lesson 2

Bennett, David. *What Am I Made of?* New York: Macmillan, 1990.

Brady, Janeen. *My Body Machine.* Salt Lake City: Brite Music, 1989.
This resource also includes an audiocassette and activity book.

Gross, Ruth B. *A Book About Your Skeleton.* Mamaroneck, N.Y.: Hastings House, 1979.

Moore, JoEllen, and Joy Evans. *My Skeleton and My Muscles.* Monterey, Calif.: Even Moore, 1987.

Pearce, Q.L. *My Body and How It Works.* New York: Tor Books, 1988.
For grades 1-3, this activity booklet contains reproducible pages and a large poster of the muscular and skeletal systems. Order from the publisher: 18 Lower Ragsdale Dr., Monterey, California 93940-5746.

Showers, Paul. *You Can't Make a Move Without Your Muscles.* New York: Crowell, 1982.

Lesson 3

Brown, Margaret W. *Nibble, Nibble: Poems for Children.* New York: Harper, 1959.
"How Do You Know?" is a poem about the senses.

Kennedy, X.J. and Dorothy. *Knock at a Star.* Boston: Little, Brown, 1982.
An excellent resource for poems about the senses. Suggestions: "My Fingers," "September," and "Mr. Wells."

Lesson 4

Cobb, Vicki. *How to Really Fool Yourself.* New York: Crowell, 1981.
A book of optical illusions.

Do You See What I See? Filmstrip/audiocassette. Clearvue.
This nine-minute film encourages students to find new ways of seeing things.

Parker, Steve. *The Eye and Seeing.* New York: Watts, 1989.
Intended for grades 5 and up, this book may be a helpful resource.

Showers, Paul. *Look at Your Eyes.* New York: Crowell, 1962.

Teaching About Vision. Schaumburg, Ill.: National Society to Prevent Blindness.
A comprehensive teaching and reference aid, which includes illustrations and extensive bibliography.

Thomson, David. *Visual Magic.* New York: Dial Books, 1991.
A collection of over thirty visual tricks and illusions involving colors, shapes, patterns, and perspective. Included are a pair of 3-D glasses.

You and Your Eyes. Filmstrip/audiocassette. Disney Educational Products.
"Explains how eight images pass through the eye and how they are transmitted into what we see."

Lesson 5

Brown, Marc. *Arthur's Eyes.* Reading Rainbow Series. Boston: Little, Brown, 1986.

Raskin, Ellen. *Spectacles*. 2nd edition. New York: Macmillan, 1988.

Wolff, Angelika. *Mom, I Need Glasses*. Batavia, Ill.: Lion Press, 1971.

Lesson 6

The Eyes Have It. Videocassette. Schaumburg, Ill.: National Society to Prevent Blindness.
> An eye safety program for early elementary level. An 8-minute film (1/2" VHS tape) presents basic safety concepts.Order from the publisher: East Remington Rd., Schaumburg, Illinois 60173.

Health - Eye Care. Videocassette. AIMS Media.
> This 11-minute color video "helps students learn to care for their eyes and protect them from injury." It tells what to do and what not to do if something gets into the eye; describes good habits for reading and watching TV, and identifies throwing objects into the faces of others and looking into the sun as unsafe.

Wood, Jean. *Eye and Ear Care*. Filmstrips/audiocassettes. Educational Activities.
> Two stories about the importance of properly caring for eyes and ears. "Princess Ocula" (16-minutes running time) tells about the unique nature of the eye and "Gullible Jeb" (15-minutes running time) about ears.

Lesson 7

Braille Alphabet and Numbers New York: American Foundation for the Blind, 1984.
> This is a 9" x 4" display card embossed with the braille alphabet and numbers. Order from the publisher: 15 West 16th St., New York, N.Y. 10011.

Cohen, Miriam. *See You Tomorrow, Charles*. New York: Greenwillow, 1983.

Corn, Anne L., and Iris Martinez. *When You Have a Visually Handicapped Child in Your Classroom: Suggestions for Teachers*. New York: American Foundation for the Blind, 1977.
> A booklet giving practical suggestions on attitudes, mobility, and materials. Free single copy.

Corn, Anne L., Chris M. Cowan, and Elaine Moses. *You Seem Like a Regular Kid to Me*. New York: American Foundation for the Blind, 1988.
> Question and answer format. A blind girl tells how she handles situations that come at home and in school. Free single copy.

Hallum, Rosemary. *Zora, the Guide Dog*. Filmstrip/audiocassette. Educational Activities.
> The true story of the life and training of a guide dog.

Keats, Ezra Jack. *Apartment 3*. New York: Macmillan, 1986.

Louis Braille. New York: American Foundation for the Blind, 1972.
> A brief biography of the inventor of the braille system of writing and reading. A 13-page booklet; single copy, free.

MacLachlan, Patricia. *Through Grandpa's Eyes*. New York: Harper, 1980.

Murphy, Jo Anne. *How Does a Blind Person Get Around?* New York: American Foundation for the Blind, 1973.
> Available at no charge, this booklet provides information about how visually impaired people get around on their own.

Newth, Philip. *Roly Goes Exploring.* New York: Putnam, 1987.
> This is a special book for children with actual braille.

Tannenbaum, Robin L. *A Different Way of Seeing.* New York: American Foundation for the Blind, 1984.
> Written as a letter to children, this free 22-page booklet describes how blind children read and write, what they do for fun, and how children can assist blind friends.

Wright, Christine. *My Sister Katie: How She Sees God's World.* Minneapolis: Augsburg, 1990.
> A day with Katie, a blind girl, as she enjoys God's world.

Yolen, Jane. *The Seeing Stick.* New York: Crowell, 1977.

Lesson 8 and 9

Parker, Steve. *The Ear and Hearing.* New York: Watts, 1989.
> This resource explains how the ear works and how to protect hearing. It includes a section on hearing aids and ear surgery. Although intended for grades 5 and above, the book may be a helpful resource.

Showers, Paul. *Ears Are for Hearing.* New York: Crowell, 1990.

You and Your Ears. Filmstrip/audiocassette. Disney Educational Products.
> "Shows how the ear and its functions make it possible for us to hear different sounds. Gives a descriptive view of every part of the ear."

Lesson 10

McGovern, Ann. *Too Much Noise.* New York: Scholastic, 1967.

Wood, Jean. *Eye and Ear Care.* Filmstrips/cassettes. Educational Activities.

Lesson 11

Costello, Elaine. *How to Speak With Your Hands.* New York: Bantam, 1983.
> Suitable for younger readers.

Kitterman, Jane, and S. Harold Collins. *A Word in the Hand: An Introduction to Sign Language.* Eugene, Ore.: Garlic Press, 1989.
> To order this resource contact the publisher at 100 Hillview, Lane #2, Eugene, Oregon 97401.

Levine, Edna S. *Lisa and Her Soundless World.* New York: Human Sciences Press, 1984.

Litchfield, Ada B. *A Button in Her Ear.* Niles, Ill.: Whitman, 1976.

Petersen, Jeanne W. *I Have a Sister, My Sister Is Deaf.* New York: Harper Trophy, 1984.

Riekehof, Lottie L. *The Joy of Signing: The Illustrated Guide for Mastering Sign Language and the Manual Alphabet.* 2nd ed. Springfield, Mo.: Gospel Publishing House, 1987.
> A resource for those who wish to teach a song or sentence in sign language.

Wolf, Bernard. *Anna's Silent World.* New York: Harper, 1984.

For more student/teacher resources on hearing impairment or deafness contact appropriate local or national organizations. Two suggestions: Deaf Children's Society of British Columbia, 3644 Slocan St., Vancouver, British Columbia V5M 3E8 and National Information Center on Deafness, Gallaudet University, 800 Florida Ave., Washington, D.C. 20002.

LESSON 1: GROWING AND CHANGING

Preparation/Materials

- For measuring activity:
  tape measures, one for each pair of students
  Student Activity
- Optional: pictures of people at different stages of growth (or a sequence of personal photographs, childhood to adult)
- Optional: arrange for parents or older students to assist with step 4

Objectives

- Students will recognize that God planned for all human beings to grow and change.
- Students will understand that each human being has a unique pattern of growth.

Background

God made all living things so that they change and grow. All living things, including humans, begin as single cells. The cells grow and then divide to form new cells. This process, called growth, continues until full development is achieved.

A variety of factors determine growth in humans. The main ones are genetic endowment, nutrition, susceptibility to disease and emotional strain, and hormonal balance. Of course, the pituitary and thyroid glands have an especially important role in growth.

• •

Lesson

1. Ask students what the difference is between themselves and some common classroom object (windows or tables, for example). Keep questioning until the students say that they are alive and the object is not. Then lead the class to see that God made all living things, human beings included, so that they change and grow.

2. Talk with students about how much they have grown since they were babies. If you have obtained pictures of people at different stages of growth, point out that people's growth patterns vary and that many different factors affect growth (for example, environmental and genetic factors). Note that although class members are about the same age, they vary in height, in the size of hands, feet, head, etc.

3. **Student activity.** Introduce the activity by recalling times when students have measured their height (at earlier grade levels or perhaps during visits to the doctor). Explain that in this lesson students will measure the size of different parts of the body.

   Turn to the activity sheet and read aloud each of the body parts they will be measuring in class. Teach new vocabulary as necessary. Then divide the class into pairs and give each pair a tape measure. Before beginning the activity, have one pair of students demonstrate how to take each of the measurements (for example, how to measure the circumference of the wrist).

   Instruct students to work with their partners to find their own measurements. Circulate around the room to offer assistance. The two students who did the demonstrating may be able to help other students take measurements, or parent or older student volunteers may be asked to help. Many students will need help in reading the measurements.

4. **Discussion and closure.** When the exercise is completed, talk about the results. Use questions such as the following:

"How many of you have the same size foot?"

"Which measurements were the easiest to take?"

"Which measurements were the most difficult to take?"

Summarize the lesson. In God's plan all living things grow and change. Each one of us is growing and changing in many ways. However, each person has his or her own growth rate and pattern.

• •

Related Activities

1. Writing center: ask students to write a paragraph about how they have changed since they started school (or were born).

2. Students may enjoy drawing a set of sequential pictures to illustrate their own growth or to illustrate how something in nature grows and changes (a plant from seed to maturity, a tree in each of the seasons, the stages of insect or butterfly life).

3. If you have not used the materials on death, consider using this lesson on growth and change as an opportunity to deal with the subject.

4. Integrate with science and study the growth of living things. Start a class "growing" project in the classroom. Have seeds or seedlings for students to plant and take care of and/or have an animal with young for them to observe.

LESSON 2: INTRODUCING BODY SYSTEMS

Preparation/Materials
- Student Activities 1 and 2 of skeletal and muscle systems

Objectives
- Students will recognize that the body has various systems.

- Students will be able to describe the muscular and skeletal systems.
- Students will react by praising and thanking God for making them "fearfully and wonderfully."

• •

Lesson

1. Start this lesson where the previous lesson ended, with a discussion of the wonderful way God has made us. Review that each person is living and growing—although each individual has his or her own growth rate and pattern. Then explain that our bodies have several intricate body systems. Define system "a set of parts or things that form a whole" and give students several examples of systems (stereo system, school system, solar system, or transportation system).

    Ask if they are aware of their body systems. Note that when the systems are working well, we aren't even aware of them. Tell students that in this lesson they will talking about some of these systems.

2. Have students feel a few of their bones—the long bones running along the front of their legs, their ankle and wrist bones, and their cheek bones.

    Refer students to Student Activity 1 picturing the bone system. Tell students that this whole bone system is called a skeleton. The skeleton gives the body shape; some bones protect other body parts (for example, the skull protects the brain). The skeleton consists of about 206 bones (many of these—about half—are bones in the hands and feet). Ask students to recall how their bones felt—hard or soft? (Bones are hard on the outside, but they are soft on the inside.) If time permits, have students color the activity page.

    Tell students that our bones keep growing. Ask: "How do we know our bones are growing?" (We become taller.) Explain that some bones will continue to grow for almost twenty years; however, a few (such as those in the inner ear) are full size at birth.

3. Next, do a brief activity to make students aware of their muscles. Have students practice tension and relaxation of muscles (from *Horizons Physical Education K-2*):
    - *Legs.* Curl toes tightly and then make all the muscles in each leg hard. Hold the position. Let it go.

- *Arms.* Clench fists tightly so that nails bite into palms. Make sure every muscle in each arm is tight. Hold. Let it all go.
- *Face.* Close eyes. Pinch them shut tightly until it almost hurts. Tense up all face muscles. Hold. Let it all go.

4. Identify that what they are tightening and relaxing are muscles. Refer students to Student Activity 2 showing body muscles. Explain that this is another body system. Explain that bones can't move by themselves and that the muscles attached to the bones make it possible for us to move. Muscles also help us breathe and swallow. Ask students if they can name one important organ of the body that is a muscle (heart). Point out that when we keep active we are exercising our muscles and making them strong. If time permits, have students color the activity page.

   Note that although everyone must have bones to hold the body up and muscles to make it move, people's bones and muscles aren't all exactly alike. Some people's muscles may be stronger than others', and some people's bones may be larger than others'.

5. Ask students to name other body systems. Name the breathing (respiratory) system (covered in more detail in the last unit in connection with smoking) and the blood (circulatory) system, and the eating/food (digestive) system.

6. **Closure.** End the lesson by stressing that it is God who gives us life and who has planned the intricacy of our bodies. Thank God in song and/or prayer. Song suggestions: "Praise and Thanksgiving" (*Children's Hymnbook*, 48), "There's No One Exactly Like Me" (*Songs to Grow On*, 57), or "If I Were a Butterfly" (*Proclaim Songbook 1*, p. 14; *Songs of God's Love*, 58). Stress that another way of thanking God is by taking good care of our bodies. Explain that in the health units that follow, students will learn more about taking care of their bodies.

• •

Related Activities

- Read books on the lesson topic and make them available in the book center. Some suggested titles are *You Can't Make a Move Without Your Muscles* by Paul Showers, *A Book About Your Skeleton* by Ruth B. Gross, *My Body Machine* by Janeen Brady, *My Body and How It Works* by Q.L. Pearce, and *What Am I Made of?* by David Bennett.

LESSON 3: REVIEW OF THE SENSES

Preparation/Materials

- For student collages:
  magazines and/or drawing materials
  five large sheets of construction paper (one
      for each sense)
  glue
- Optional: one picture to illustrate each of
  the senses

Objectives

- Students will review the five senses and
  describe what each sense does.
- Students will recognize that the senses are
  interdependent.

Lesson

1. Name some things that people may enjoy doing (or name some things that you enjoy)
   —for example, listening to music, eating strawberries, petting kittens, smelling flowers,
   or watching the snow fall. Or show the class pictures illustrating the senses. Have students recall each of the five senses and how each is used. Then have them identify
   which sense is used in each enjoyable activity or picture.

   Use the examples to explain how the senses work together. When we eat strawberries,
   for example, what senses are involved?

2. As a review activity, have the class make a display of the senses. Divide the class into
   five groups. Assign each group to make a collage representing one of the senses. They
   should cut out magazine pictures or draw pictures about the sense. Then each group
   should paste their pictures on a large sheet of construction paper. Add captions to the
   completed collages and display them in the classroom.

3. **Closure.** Have members of each group explain their pictures. Tell students that the next
   few lessons will be about eyes and ears and how to take care of them.

Related Activities

1. Enjoy poems about the senses. Write the
   class's favorite on a chart to memorize or to
   use as a choral reading. Poem suggestions:
   "How Do You Know?" by Margaret Wise
   Brown in *Nibble, Nibble;* "My Fingers" by
   Mary O'Neill, "September" by John Updike,
   and "Mr. Wells" by Elizabeth Madox
   Roberts in *Knock at a Star* by X. J. and
   Dorothy Kennedy.

2. Take a sense walk with the class. Focus on
   looking, listening, smelling, and touching.
   Add tasting by providing students with
   slices of apple to munch on. After the walk
   brainstorm lists of sensory experiences, or
   have students write individual lists and
   then write a paragraph describing what
   they saw, heard, smelled, touched , and
   tasted.

3. Play a guessing game. Class members can take turns describing something by the way it looks, smells, sounds, feels, or tastes. The rest of the class guesses what is being described.

4. Writing center: put up posters, magazine pictures, or art reproductions as inspirations for student poems or stories. Also write out these questions: "What do you see?" "What do you hear?" "What does it taste like?" "How does it feel?" "What do you smell?"

    Students should choose one picture and imagine what it would be like to be standing in it. Then they should write about what they would hear, see, feel, smell, or taste there. Number the pictures so that students can indicate which one they're writing about.

5. Have the class explore a food item using all five of their senses. (Choose something crunchy like an apple or popcorn so hearing is included.) Write about it individually or as a class.

LESSON 4: THE MIRACLE OF VISION

Preparation/Materials

- Teacher visual of the eye
- Make a mobile with cards on which are written the lesson vocabulary.
- Hand mirrors, one for every student or pair of students
- Student Activities 1 and 2

Objectives

- Students will identify the front parts of the eye.
- Students will be able to describe ways our eyes help us.

• •

Lesson

1. Recall that eyes are one of the sense organs. Define and teach the word *vision* (the sense that allows us to know the color, shape, and size of an object). Explain that when we see, our eyes look at patterns of light. The eyes send these patterns to the brain. When the brain receives the message, we see the paper, pencil, our lunch, or our bike. So vision is seeing something with our eyes and knowing what it is with our brain.

2. Show students the picture of the eye and ask them to identify any parts of the eye that they can. Point out the parts and what each does: eyebrows and eyelashes (made of little hairs; keep dust or other particles out of the eye), eyelids (shades to keep out light; protects from dust, etc.), pupil (dark spot in center that lets in light), iris (colored area; color is inherited; changes size of pupil), and sclera (white part that covers most of our eye; shapes and protects). Students may identify and fill in the blanks on Student Activity 1 as you discuss the teacher visual.

    You may want to explain that there are other important parts to the eye that we can't see from the front (for example, retina, optic nerve, and eye muscle) and these parts are just as important as the parts we can see. Also differentiate between parts of the eye that help us see (pupil, iris) and parts that help to clean and protect the eye (eyelids, eyelashes, eyebrows).

    Explain that tears come from a tear gland at the top of the eye and that tears keep our eyes wet and help to keep the eye clean. Every time we blink, our eyelids spread a layer of tears over the eye. When we cry, the "extra" tears drain through a passage into the nose.

    Have students feel the bony structure around their eyes. Ask: "Why do you think we have those bones around our eyes?" (To protect the eyes.)

3. Brainstorm a list of ways our eyes help us. Include the following and elicit from students specific examples of each. For example, our eyes help us (1) enjoy the beauty of creation, (2) learn about creation, and (3) keep us safe and protect from danger (seeing where we're going, avoiding approaching cars, reading warning labels, signs, and traffic lights).

4. **Student activity.** Turn to the worksheet and distribute the mirrors. Ask students to look carefully (pairs take turns) at their eyes in the mirror and find the pupil, iris, and sclera. Then have students complete the sheets individually or in pairs, or if the activity sheet seems difficult for your class, do this as a whole class activity.

5. **Closure:** "Today we learned something about our amazing eyes. We learned the names of some parts of the eye and what these parts do. In the next lessons we'll talk about taking care of our eyes."

• •

Related Activities

1. Have students practice using their eyes for careful observation. Ask students to closely observe an object or person in the classroom. Then call on students to give their description. The rest of the class must guess what or who the description was about.

2. Study all the parts of the eye and how the eye "works." Read a book to the class on the topic. You may wish to make a cassette recording of the book and put the recording and the book at a center. Students can listen to the text and follow along in the book. One good choice is *Look at Your Eyes* by Paul Showers.

3. Have fun with optical illusions. Two good resources are Vicki Cobb's *How to Really Fool Yourself* and David Thomson's *Visual Magic.*

4. Bring in a live animal (a snake or bird) or an interesting object from nature (some-thing with fascinating shapes and textures) for the class to observe. Have the students spend time observing and describing what they see. Then pass out a large sheet of paper (at least 11" x 17") to each student. Instruct the students to draw all or part of the object they observed. The only instruction they must follow is that the drawing must touch each side of the paper (to get them thinking big and inspire them to include a lot of details). Will they be able to see what "only a planner could plan"?

5. Find and display close-up photos of parts of things and have the children guess what it is. (Such pictures are often included in *Highlights* magazine and in children's books.)

6. Center class devotions on Psalm 101:6 or on Psalm 139:16 which both speak in a comforting way of the Lord's eyes being on us.

LESSON 5: EYE CHECKUPS

Preparation/Materials

- Filmstrip or slides and appropriate projector (see Step 1)
- Story to read about wearing glasses
- Optional: eye chart for vision testing
- Optional: invite a school nurse or other health professional to explain the purpose of vision testing.

Objectives

- Students will identify the purpose of vision testing and wearing glasses.
- Students will empathize with those who have glasses.

Lesson

1. Set up a filmstrip or picture on an overhead or slide projector before class and have it purposely set out of focus. When class begins, proceed to talk about what you are showing as if the class should be able to see it. Ask questions about details in the projected picture. When the students are unable to respond correctly, explain that they can't answer because the picture is out of focus. Tell them that this could be what things would look like if they needed glasses. Then focus the projector and ask "Can everyone clearly see the picture now?" Explain that a glass lens can change how we see things. That's why wearing glasses can help some people see better. If we see fine, wearing glasses might make things look worse. An eye doctor can decide if we need glasses and if we do what type we should wear.

2. Ask volunteers to describe how doctors have examined their eyes during a routine health checkup. Note that if things we see are blurred or if our eyes burn, we usually go to a special doctor, an eye doctor.

3. Discuss the purpose of eye tests. If possible, display an eye chart and have a health professional explain the importance of vision testing and of obtaining glasses if necessary.

   Talk about how glasses can correct vision problems. Ask: "How would your feel if you had trouble seeing clearly?" "How would your feel after you got glasses that helped your eyes and corrected the problem?" Volunteers who wear glasses may wish to tell about the difference glasses made for them—and how they knew they needed glasses.

4. Read and discuss a children's book on the topic of getting glasses and the difference glasses can make. Suggested titles: *Arthur's Eyes* by Marc Brown, *Spectacles* by Ellen Raskin, or *Mom, I Need Glasses* by Angelika Wolff.

5. **Closure.** Summarize and reflect on the lesson with questions such as "Why are eye checkups important?" "How did glasses help (main character of Step 4 book)?" "What are some signs that tell us that we may need an eye checkup?"

●●

Related Activities

1. Have students collect old glasses from friends and relatives to send to countries where glasses are very expensive and difficult to obtain. Contact local service organizations for information about whom to work through and where to send the glasses.

2. Set up a center with an eye chart and several old pairs of glasses for the students to try on.

LESSON 6: EYE SAFETY

Preparation/Materials
- Chart paper
- Student Activity
- Optional: objects to demonstrate eye safety rules—spray can, goggles, scissors, guard strap for glasses, small lamp or light bulb

Objective
- Students will describe practices that help prevent eye injury.

Lesson

1. Begin by describing a time you had sand or dirt in your eye or by asking students to recall such a time. Follow up with questions: "How did your eye respond? (Blinking and tearing.) Why do you think your eye did that?" (For protection; to wash out the object.)

2. Discuss what to do and what not to do if something gets in the eye. Stress that students should not rub the eye. Instead, they should blink or pull down the eyelid to start a flow of tears to help wash the dirt out. If this doesn't take care of the problem, they should promptly tell an adult.

3. Brainstorm ways to take care of the eyes, ways to prevent injury (students can do this in groups). Have students explain how each rule helps keep eyes safe. Another option is to hold up a series of objects (spray can, goggles, scissors, guard strap for glasses, small lamp or light bulb) and have students think of the safety rule that each object suggests. Use group suggestions to make a class list of safety rules. Write the rules on chart paper. Include the following safety rules:
   - Point sharp objects away from your own or others' eyes. Discuss how to safely hold and use scissors and other sharp tools.
   - Be careful around spray cans (hairspray, for example). Don't use sprays without permission, and always spray away from eyes. Protect eyes from household cleaning products.
   - Protect eyes with goggles during activities where eyes may be at risk.
   - Those who wear glasses need to wear a strap during games and sports. Also during active play try to avoid hitting the glasses of other participants.
   - Don't play with firecrackers.
   - Don't hit or poke anyone in the eye.
   - Use good lighting when reading or doing other close work.
   - Don't look directly at the sun or at a sun lamp.
   - Get enough rest.

Add the two rules covered earlier in the lesson:
- Blink if we get dirt in the eye to let tears wash it out; don't rub.
- Tell an adult if we have an eye problem.

Post the rules in the classroom.

4. **Student activity.** Use the activity sheet to review ways to protect eyesight. Students draw a line to connect each picture with the words that tell how to protect eyes.

5. **Closure.** Reflect in the lesson with questions such as these:
   - "What rule is the hardest for you to follow? Why?"
   - "What is one of the most important things you've learned about eyes in this lesson (unit)?"

LESSON 7: VISUAL IMPAIRMENT

Preparation/Materials
- Story about someone with serious visual impairment or blindness to read to the class
- Make a large braille alphabet chart (modeled on student activity).
- Student Activity
- Optional: invite a visually impaired or blind person to speak to the class about how he or she writes and reads.
- Optional: obtain a braille watch and/or a braille book.
- Optional: contact the local branch of American Foundation for the Blind or the National Society for the Prevention of Blindness for educational materials or student handouts.

Objectives
- Students will describe problems that people who are blind or visually impaired may have.
- Students will identify ways in which blind/visually impaired people are similar to those who are normally sighted.
- Students will identify braille as the method used by blind people to read and write.

Lesson

1. Discuss visual impairments or disabilities. Explain that some people who are visually impaired may have very poor or low vision but can tell the difference between light and dark or can see shapes. Others are totally blind and can't see at all. (If students are curious about how people become visually disabled, explain that some are born blind or with impairment, but the sight of others may be lost or impaired by disease or accident. In old age vision often weakens, too.)

2. Have children close their eyes and imagine they can't see. What can they use to orient themselves? Have them feel different objects near them and describe their textures (desk top, their own shirt or blouse, shoes, socks). Lead students to understand that those who are blind have to depend more on their other senses, especially on hearing and touch. Since visually impaired or blind people are often treated as though they are also deaf or unintelligent, stress what visually impaired people have in common with normally sighted people.

    Ask: "If you were blind, how do you think you would find your toys or clothes?" Give students time to think through the situation. Explain that children who are blind need to be especially neat and keep their things in the same place so that they can find them. Ask students to figure out how they could find what clothes they wanted to wear if they couldn't see their clothes (sense of touch, remembering order of placement in closet, markings in braille to indicate color). Next consider how children who are blind find the food on their plate. (They imagine the plate is a clock. Someone tells them at what time such food is placed.) Illustrate with a sketch on the blackboard.

Ask: "How could you explain to a blind classmate how to find his or her hamburger? French fries? Tomato?"

3. Read a book such as *Roly Goes Exploring* by Philip Newth, *Through Grandpa's Eyes* by Patricia MacLachlan, *The Seeing Stick* by Jane Yolen, or Ezra Keats's *Apartment 3*. Use the story as a basis for discussion of blindness and serious visual impairment.

   If you have invited a resource person to your classroom, ask him or her to speak about dealing with visual disability, and read the book later to reinforce concepts.

   In the resource person's presentation or in the discussion cover devices available to help blind people move around and to read and write. Stress the heightened reliance on other senses. Emphasize what the visually handicapped can do: attend college and hold a variety of jobs (for example, computer programmer, piano tuner, lawyer, store manager, among many others).

4. If you have obtained braille books or a watch, give students the opportunity to feel and examine the items. Then introduce the braille alphabet. Explain that instead of using the sense of sight, blind people use their sense of touch to read. Tell students that braille is a language of raised dots (combinations of six raised dots), read by the fingers. It dates from 1824 when it was made by Louis Braille. (Braille was produced with a sharp stylus that punches indentations onto paper fitted over a metal slate. Today lightweight portable tools and braille typewriters are available).

5. **Student activity.** Have students complete the activity. To raise the dots, have students place the activity sheet on a tablet face down and go over each dot with a dull pencil (press heavily). Then turn the paper over and feel the raised dots. If you prefer, have students put dabs of craft glue on the dots (dry before touching) to give the raised effect. The message on the lower half of the activity sheet is "Braille is a way of reading."

6. **Closure.** Write the sentence starter: "Today I learned..." on the board. Have students complete the sentence orally. See how many different sentence endings they can come up with.

• •

Related Activities

1. Have pairs of students write messages to each other in braille.

2. Research how visually impaired or blind people get around. Students will enjoy learning about the work and training of guide dogs. Consider showing and discussing the filmstrip *Zora, the Guide Dog,* which tells the true story of one dog's life and training.

LESSON 8: MIRACLE OF HEARING

Preparations/Materials
- TV or video recording and VCR
- Student Activities 1 and 2
- Teacher visual
- For demonstrating how sound waves travel:
  tuning fork
  glass of water
- Optional: pictures of animals with various types of ears

Objectives
- Students will describe the connection between sounds and feeling, understanding, and communicating.
- Students will learn the basic structure and function of the ear.

• •

Lesson

1. Turn on the TV or play part of a video recording for students; don't turn on the sound. Then play the same segment with sound and ask students to describe the difference. How did the sound help them know what was happening? Did any sounds tell them things they couldn't see? Were some of the sounds exciting, enjoyable, funny? How do certain sounds affect our feelings? (Examples: happy singing, laughing, crying, yelling, absolute silence, purring or meowing of a cat.) Tell students that the next few lessons are going to be about their sense of hearing.

   Alternate option: Ask students to pretend they are lying in bed during a thunderstorm. Even if the curtains are closed and they can't see the storm, how do they know what's happening? Have them describe what they hear during a bad storm. Continue the activity, giving examples of other situations to imagine.

2. Use pictures of animals to discuss the shape of the visible part of the ear called the pinna. Or ask students to come to the board and draw pictures of the ears of well-known animals such as rabbits, cats, dogs (various kinds of ears), elephants. Then ask them students to draw a human ear. Point out that most large animals have ears which stand away from their heads. Often they move their ears to point towards sounds in order to tell from which direction danger may be coming. Ask students if they've noticed animals pricking up their ears and then going to investigate.

   Contrast with human ears which are flatter and smaller and move little or not at all. These ears, say scientists, are best for hearing all sorts of sounds from different directions at once. We have two ears, one on each side of the head, so that we can tell which direction the sound is coming from. (Our brain figures out the position of the sound by comparing sound waves reaching each ear.)

3. Use the teacher visual of the ear to explain how we hear. Point out each part of the ear on the visual and give its name as you come to it. Have students complete Student Activity 1 in their workbooks as you explain the visual of the ear. (Write names of parts on the board as each is mentioned if the visual is difficult for students to see). Here is a simple explanation for your reference.
   - Outer ear. Consists of two parts: the *pinna* and *ear* (or auditory) *canal*. Your outer ear is your sound-catcher. The sounds it picks up go through the ear canal to middle part of your ear.
   - Middle ear. The sound goes through the ear canal and hits your *eardrum*. The sounds make your eardrum jiggle (vibrate). The motion passes on to three tiny bones—the *hammer, anvil,* and *stirrup.*
   - Inner ear. The sounds then travel on to your inner ear to the cochlea which has fluid in it. The cochlea, shaped like a snail shell, has tiny, tiny hairs that connect to nerves that send the motion (via the auditory nerve) to the hearing center in your brain.
   - Your *brain* tells you what you're hearing. Note that listening is part of hearing, just as looking is part of seeing. We can hear without listening. We hear with our ears, but we listen with our mind.

   Explain that our ears are also important for our sense of balance (and sense of pressure—as when we're in a fast-moving elevator). Our balance is controlled in the inner ear. Three curved canals (called the semicircular canals) or tubes that contain fluid control our balance.

4. Use a tuning fork to demonstrate how sound waves move.
   - Have the class listen to the sounds made when you strike a tuning fork. Explain what happens. The movement or vibration makes sound waves. Again refer to the visual to trace the path of the sound through the various parts of their ears and on to the brain. After you strike the fork let students feel the vibrations.
   - After striking the tuning fork hold it to water in a glass to demonstrate how the sound waves set off by the vibrations can move through water.

   Summarize by telling students that sounds (ring of telephone, drumbeat, whisper, shout) move the air around them. When you hear a sound, you're really hearing the air move. A big sound moves air a lot; a little sound moves air a little.

5. **Student activity.** Have students complete Student Activity 2. If this is difficult have students work in pairs in full class session.
   Answers: (1) pinna, sound; (2) eardrum; (3) hammer, anvil, stirrup; (4) inner; (5) brain, hear.

6. **Closure.** Tell the class that hearing is another example of how wonderfully God has designed our bodies. Our ears are strange looking things really, but they are designed to do something complicated and amazing.

Related Activities

1. Show films and/or read books on the lesson topic. *You and Your Ears* is a film suggestion; *Ears Are for Hearing* by Paul Showers is one book suggestion.

2. Center idea: make an audio recording of different sounds and put it at a center for the children to listen to. If possible, record sounds of places with which the children are familiar (classroom, gym, gas station or grocery store, fast food restaurant). Allow time between each sound or each group of sounds for them to jot down what they think each sound is or where they think the group of sounds was made. Discuss the activity: Was it hard to identify places/sounds or easy? Which sounds were the most difficult and why?

3. Write poems about favorite sounds. (See Related Activity in Unit 3, Lesson 6 for ideas.)

LESSON 9: HEARING AND SAFETY

Objective
- Students will identify ways sounds help keep us safe.

Lesson

1. Begin the lesson by making a few sounds that warn of danger. Be dramatic! Then have the class identify what was going on or what the sound was. Lead into a discussion of how our sense of hearing helps to keep us safe.

2. Have students working in groups make lists of warning sounds that help keep us safe. What are some warning sounds and what do they tell us? (Sirens of fire trucks and other emergency vehicles, car horns, bicycle bells, train and boat whistles and horns, thunder, growl of a dog or hiss of a cat, police officers' whistles, fire alarms, smoke alarms, crash of falling rocks or branches, fog horns, footsteps, kettle whistles, roar of a lion, rattle of rattlesnake, sound of approaching car, sound of breaking ice, truck back-up warning.) If necessary, give students an idea or two to get started. Appoint one person in each group to write down the sounds and another to read the completed list to the class.

3. Combine the group suggestions into one list on the board or on a chart. Then brainstorm additional sounds. Identify how each helps to keep us safe.

4. **Student activity.** Integrate with language arts and assign students to write stories about an incident in which the sense of hearing helped keep someone safe. Have them refer to the list of sounds to get a story idea. Provide a story starter that gives characters and settings. ("My name is Albert. Yesterday my class went on a great trip to _____.")

5. **Closure.** Summarize the lesson or elicit a summary from the students.

Related Activities

1. Display a large picture (sports event, city scene, family dinner) and talk about what's happening in the picture. Ask: "Suppose you were in the picture, what would you hear?" Ask class members (individually or in groups) to create sounds they would hear.

2. Center idea: explain that Morse Code can be used to send messages over long distances (with the help of electricity). Operators change written messages into a code that uses different combinations of dots and dashes. The message the receiver hears is a combination of short and long clicks;

the dots are short clicks and the dashes are long clicks. The receiver uses the code to figure out the message and puts it into written words.

Make a diagram of Morse Code (found in most encyclopedias) and put it at the center. On a sheet of paper provide several simple sentences for students to translate into Morse Code. Or have each students make up a few simple sentences and then have a partner figure out what the sentence is. Provide a block and pen or pencil for tapping out the code.

3. Students can use puppets to act out the stories created in Step 4. Divide the class into small groups and have them choose a story written by one of their group to dramatize.

LESSON 10: TAKING CARE OF OUR HEARING

Preparation/Materials
- A washcloth
- Pictures of extremely noisy environments (planes taking off, power lawnmowers, music group with amplifiers) and extremely quiet environments
- Student Activity
- Optional: an audiometer and a hearing technician to demonstrate
- Optional: chart paper

Objectives
- Students will identify ways to protect their sense of hearing.
- Students will choose to follow safety rules and protect their hearing.

· ·

Lesson

1. Explain that the last lesson stressed how much we depend on our sense of hearing and how our sense of hearing helps us to enjoy the world God made. This lesson is about how we can take care of our sense of hearing.

2. Go over ways to protect our sense of hearing. Write the ways on the board or on a chart.
   - Don't put objects in your ear. Ask students if they know the basic rule for ear care (never put anything small into their ear—even to clean it). A safe way to clean ears is to use a washcloth wrapped around a finger. Demonstrate or have a volunteer demonstrate with a washcloth.
   - Be careful about objects in the ear. Ask: "Have you ever gotten something in your ear that you couldn't get out? What did you do?" Explain that poking at the object only makes it worse because the ear canal gets smaller, and poking just wedges it in tighter. Stress that one should not try to get the object out but should tell an adult.
   - Promptly report earaches to an adult for treatment. Briefly discuss earaches. Give students opportunity to talk about their experiences with earaches. What did their parents do? What did the doctor do? Stress that earaches shouldn't be ignored; students should report an earache promptly so that it can be treated.
   - Protect your ears from loud noises. Show the pictures of extremely noisy and extremely quiet situations. Elicit from students how they feel or act in the various situations. Students will probably say that the extremely noisy situations make them want to go away or cover their ears. Explain that too much loud noise—and especially noise with very high loud sounds—can hurt our ears if we are exposed to the sound for a long period of time. (The cells in the cochlea of the inner ear can be damaged.) People who use power equipment or work around heavy machinery should cover their ears to protect their hearing.

- Cover your ears in very cold weather. Ask students whether there is special care for ears depending on the weather. Explain that in very cold weather it's a good idea to protect our ears. That's one reason people wear hats or ear muffs in winter cold.

3. Demonstrate or discuss ear testing. Ask: "Have you every had your ears tested? Do you remember what the test was like?" Talk about the testing procedure (listening to sounds of varying volume and pitch) and if a resource person is present, ask him or her to demonstrate how to use the audiometer. Note that if someone can't hear clearly or has frequent earaches, it's important to have a checkup.

4. **Student activity.** Together read the safety rules printed on the side of the activity sheet. Ask students to cut along the dotted line and cut apart the safety rules. Have them study the pictures, decide the safety rule that belongs with each picture, and paste the rule in the space provided. Go over the completed activity with the class, eliciting from students the reason for each rule.

5. **Closure:** "God made each of us able to choose. Today we learned about some things we can choose to do to protect our sense of hearing. Which of these things do you think are the hardest for you to do or to remember to do?"

. . . .

Related Activities

- Study noise pollution and its effect on hearing. Have students identify ways they can help to prevent noise pollution. One resource is Ann McGovern's *Too Much Noise*.

LESSON 11: HEARING IMPAIRMENT

Preparation/Materials
- Book about hearing impairment/deafness to read to the class
- Hearing aid or, if possible, different types of hearing aids

Objectives
- Students will empathize with people who are deaf or have hearing impairments.
- Students will identify devices to help the hearing impaired and methods to overcome communication difficulties.

• •

Lesson

1. Read a few sentences or a paragraph to the class in a normal voice. Then have the students cover their ears while you read the paragraph again. Or cover your mouth with your hand as you read. Talk about how the sound is deadened. Make the point that people with hearing loss may hear sounds as muffled or distorted.

2. Read a story about someone with a hearing impairment. Some current titles are *Lisa and Her Soundless World* by Edna Levine, *Anna's Silent World* by Bernard Wolf, *I Have a Sister, My Sister Is Deaf* by Jeanne W. Peterson, or *A Button in Her Ear* by Ada Litchfield.

3. Use the story as a basis for discussion of people with deafness or with hearing impairment. Stress or elicit from children how the main character in the book is like people with normal hearing. Then identify the problems the character must cope with because of hearing loss.

4. Show the class the hearing aid and discuss how this device helps the hearing impaired. Explain that hearing loss may be slight, serious, or total. People with severe or total hearing loss go to special schools to learn special skills such as how to lip read and how to use finger spelling or sign language.

5. Explain and try lip reading. Mouth the name of one of the students and add a simple request to open the door or to stand up. Have students guess who you are talking to and what the request is.

6. Consider how we can help those who don't hear well. (For example, look at them so they can see our lips, speak clearly, repeat if necessary.)

7. Ask students to write this sentence starter on a sheet of paper "I learned that..." Then direct them to complete the sentence by writing something they have learned about being deaf or being hearing impaired. Have students share with the class the things

they have learned. Consider making this a unit review and have pairs of students work together to think of things they've learned in the course of the unit. Go over the statements in full class session. Add or fill in important concepts the class may have missed.

8. **Closure.** Highlight a few of the "I learned" statements. Discuss how these can be the impetus for making healthy choices or empathizing with others?

• •

Related Activities

1. Learn about sign language, in which each gesture expresses a particular idea or concept. Contact a local organization for the blind/visually impaired or obtain one of the resources suggested for this lesson. Or learn some letters from the manual alphabet (found in most encyclopedias) and teach students to spell some words with these hand symbols. One good sign language resource is *A Word in the Hand* by Kitterman and Collins.

2. Integrate with language arts. Ask students to pretend to be a character in the book read in step 1—for example, a sibling of the main character. Have them write a story about something that might have happened later in the life of the main character.

3. Center idea: make an audio recording of one of the books listed in step 1. Put the recording and the book at a center so students can follow along in the book as they listen to the recording.

Unit 5

Building Healthy Habits

Goals

- Students will recognize the importance and purpose of basic health habits.
- Students will choose to establish good health habits.

Background

This unit deals with basic personal health care issues—fitness, nutrition, good grooming, and dental care. The stress is on helping students become aware of the health choices they make each day, so that from a young age they begin to assume responsibility for taking care of their bodies and form healthy patterns of living. But beyond developing basic living skills and healthy habits, students need to understand why taking care of bodies is important.

North American society sends confusing signals to children about the value of a person's body. On the one hand, there is the body cult, which makes an idol of the body. Shaping, strengthening, clothing, decorating, and gratifying the body is the central focus of some people's lives. This is a form of self-glorification and of self-idolatry. On the other hand, our society has large numbers of persons who treat their bodies carelessly, ignoring basic nutrition and physical exercise or living at a too-strenuous pace. Carried to an extreme, this view leads to self-destruction. These contrasting views, however, share an underlying attitude that says, "This is my body. And what I do with my body is my business."

Christians believe that because "we are not our own," how we treat our bodies is not an individual matter. The kingly rule of Christ extends over the body, too. The body must not become an idol, but it should be treated with respect. After all, God created the human body and breathed life into it. In fact, God charged humans to be caretakers of that creation (Genesis 1:28). As God's people we are called to care for the body and use it in the service of God and others.

Vocabulary

Integrate the following suggested vocabulary:

habit	menu	respect	plaque	nutrition
bacteria	grooming	cavity	snack	balanced diet
active	endurance	germs	flossing	dentist
fit/fitness	breakfast	lunch	serving	
dental	energy	dentist	dentist	

Unit Resources

An Early Start to Good Health. Kit. New York: The American Cancer Society, 1977.
   Part 3 of this kit, My Health, is suggested for grade 2 level. Including a filmstrip/audiocassette and teacher guide, the material is a mini-musical about Healthman (a Superman look-alike) and about choosing good health habits. Piano and vocal score are included so that children can learn the song "Healthman." Contact your local Cancer Society to obtain the kit.

Color Me Red! American Alliance for Health, Physical Education, Recreation & Dance.
  An activity book on heart health for children in grades K-3. Available from AAHPERD, 1900 Association Drive, Reston, Virginia 22091; phone 800-321-0789.

Concepts for Feeling Good. Reston, Va.: AAHPERD.
  A handbook for adults, providing background information for 12 important areas of wellness.

Cooper, Kenneth H. *Kid Fitness: A Complete Shape-Up Program from Birth Through High School.*
New York: Bantam, 1991.
  Cooper, concerned for this "generation of unfit children," has produced a total program of diet and exercise designed "to dramatically increase overall physical fitness and self-esteem and foster healthy eating habits." A checklist of tests is included to gauge the child's level of physical health.

Fitness Discovery Activities. Reston, Va.: AAHPERD.
  "A series of 55 illustrative discovery activities help both adults and children learn about fitness, nutrition, stress, body composition, smoking, and other topics.

Lungs Are for Life-2. New York: American Lung Association, 1984.
  Level 2 material includes lessons on making good health choices. Teacher guide and reproducible activity sheets. Available from local chapter or contact American Lung Association, 1740 Broadway, New York, New York 10019.

Mr. Know-It-Owl's Health Tips. Videocassette. Apollo.
  Intended for ages 5-10, the video includes these unit-related segments: "Junk Food Man," "Try It, You'll Like It," and "Magic Weapons for Healthy Teeth." Available from KIMBO, Dept. 8, P.O. Box 447, Long Branch, New Jersey 07740-0477; phone 800-631-2187.

Lesson Resources

Lesson 1
Brown, Laurie, Krasny and Marc. *Dinosaurs Alive and Well! A Guide to Good Health.* Boston: Little, Brown, 1990.

Lessons 2-3
Berenstain, Stan and Jan. *The Berenstain Bears and Too Much TV.* New York: Random, 1984.

Getting to Know Your Heart. Kit. American Heart Association, 1989.
  For grades 1-3, this program has three modules: Your Heart and How It Works, Smoking and Your Body, and Food, Fun, and Fitness. Includes a teacher guide, activity suggestions, and a variety of support materials. Contact your local chapter to find out how to obtain the kit.

K-3 Games. Basic Skills Series. Gloucester, Ont.: Canadian Association for Health, Physical Education and Recreation (CAHPER).
  This 100-page resource contains activities sequenced from simple to complex. Order from CAHPER, 1600 James Naismith Drive, Gloucester, Ontario K1B 5N4; phone 613-748-5622.

Stinson, Sue. *Dance for Young Children: Finding the Magic in Movement.* American Alliance for Health, Physical Education, Recreation & Dance, 1988.

Ziefert, Harriet. *When the TV Broke.* New York: Puffin, 1989.
  Jeffrey's TV breaks and he discovers other interests.

Zuidema, Marvin A., and others. *Physical Education K-2*. Grand Rapids: Christian Schools International, 1974, 1982.

Lessons 4-8
Canada's Food Guide. (Available from Health and Welfare, Canada.)

Food … Gives Me Energy. Rosemont, Ill.: National Dairy Council, 1987.
This curriculum for grade 2 developed by the National Dairy Council provides 9 lessons on nutrition. Colorful visuals. Activities reproducible for classroom use. Ordering address: National Dairy Council, Nutrition Education Division, 6300 North River Road, Rosemont, Illinois 60019-9922.

Nutrition Around the Clock. Filmstrips. Disney Educational Media.
Consists of five filmstrips. (Distributed in Canada by McIntyre Educational Media.)

Posters of Food Groups and other classroom materials. Available from Dairy Bureau of Canada, 20 Holly St., Suite 400, Toronto M4S 3B1; phone 416-485-4453.

Sharmat, Marjorie. *Gregory, the Terrible Eater*. New York: Macmillan, 1980.

Lesson 9
Exercise and Rest. Barr Films, 1983.

Hopkins, Lee Bennett, compiler. *Go to Bed! A Book of Bedtime Poems*. New York: Knopf, 1979.
"Going to Bed" by Marchette Chute, "Bedtime" by Eleanor Farjeon, and "Charlie's Bedtime" by Lee Hopkins are some poems to enjoy with this lesson.

Isaacs, Gwynne L. *While You Are Asleep*. New York: Walker Publishing, 1991.
Although targeted for grades 4-8, this resource is helpful for teachers.

Khalsa, Dayal Kaur. *Sleepers*. New York: Crown, 1988.

McPhail, David. *The Dream Child*. New York: Dutton, 1985.

Showers, Paul. *Sleep Is for Everyone*. Let's-Read-and-Find-Out Science Book. New York: Crowell, 1974.

Ziefert, Harriet. *I Won't Go to Bed!* Boston: Little, Brown, 1987.

_____. *Good Night, Everyone!* Boston: Little, Brown, 1988.

Lesson 10
Cleanliness. Barr Films, 1985.

Cobb, Vicki. *Keeping Clean*. New York: Harper, 1989.

Health and Cleanliness. Teaching Picture Set. Marvel.
This resource consists of 12 pictures (10" x 13") and a 24-page teacher manual. Order from the publisher: Suite 1303, 212 Fifth Ave., New York, New York 10010.

Munsch, Robert. *Mud Puddle*. Toronto: Annick Press, 1982.

Lessons 11-12

Berenstain, Stan and Jan. *The Berenstain Bears Visit the Dentist.* New York: Random, 1983.

Brown, Marc. *Arthur's Tooth.* Boston: Little, Brown 1980.

Cole, Joanna. *The Missing Tooth.* Step into Reading Books. New York: Random, 1988.

Elementary School Dental Poster Set. Chicago: American Dental Association.
    Colorful posters available separately or in sets.

First Teeth. Ottawa: Canadian Dental Association.
    Kits for children (up to age 9) to promote good dental health. Contact the Canadian Dental Association for the kits and a catalog of new arrivals: 1815 Alta Vista Dr., Ottawa, Ontario K1G 3Y6.

Learning About Your Oral Health: A Prevention-Orented School Program, Level 1. Chicago: American Dental Association, 1980.
    Provides teaching units for grades K-3, including activities and several transparencies.

McPhail, David. *The Bear's Toothache.* Boston: Little, Brown, 1972.
    A humorous story that adds a lighthearted touch to the topic of teeth.

Meet Your Teeth. Filmstrip/audiocassette. Disney Educational Products.
    This filmstrip (seven-minute running time) explains what different types of teeth children will develop.

Mouth Models. Chicago: American Dental Association.
    Oversized models to demonstrate brushing techniques.

Safety of the Mouth. Filmstrip/audiocassette. Disney Educational Products.
    A six-minute film that explains how to avoid accidents that can cause serious tooth injury.

Showers, Paul. *How Many Teeth?* New York: Crowell, 1962.

Toothbrushing with Charlie Brown. Videocassette. Chicago: American Dental Association.
    This five-minute video is one of several videos on tooth care available from the Dental Association.

Why Visit the Dentist? Filmstrip/audiocassette. Disney Educational Products.
    This seven-minute filmstrip stresses the importance of visiting the dentist regularly.

LESSON 1: HEALTHY HABITS

Preparation/Materials
- Health puppet
- Plan a puppet script to dramatize good and bad habits.
- Student Activity

Objectives
- Students will identify good and bad habits.
- Students will become aware of their own good, bad, and neutral habits.
- Students will choose to work to change bad habits.

Background
A habit is a long-term practice that is consciously or unconsciously repeated. Once a practice turns into a habit, we often no longer consider the purpose or effect of it. We are on "automatic." For this reason, establishing good health habits at a young age is very important.

● ●

Lesson

1. Ask: "What is a habit?" (Something a person does regularly.) Ask students whether they have habits. Note that everyone has habits, and give an example of a typical habit or tell about one of your habits. Sometimes we don't even realize we've developed certain habits until someone else calls it to our attention.

2. Brainstorm a list of common habits and write the list on the board. Encourage each class member to contribute at least one example. Go over the list with the class and decide whether a habit is good or bad. Some habits may not fall in either category.

3. Use Alex to illustrate various habits. Have Alex tell you and the class about part or all of a day's routine. (Alternative option: describe the routine of an imaginary person for the class.) Include a few good habits (making the bed in the morning and brushing teeth) and a few bad habits (biting fingernails, dumping school things right inside the door, not eating breakfast), and some that are neither (sleeping in one position, always drinking juice before eating toast, and standing in the same spot to wait for the bus). Have Alex also act out some good and bad classroom habits. Ask the students to identify which habits are good, which bad, and which are neither good nor bad.

4. Ask: "How do we develop habits? (By doing the same thing over and over until we do it almost without thinking.) How do we break bad habits?" (By deciding we want to stop a certain action or practice and then by sticking to the decision; by substituting a good habit for it). Point out to students that new habits—new patterns—can be hard to establish, but once they are established, habits can be hard to change. Note that sometimes we develop habits by imitating what our parents and friends do. Stress that good habits can help us stay healthy and that in this unit the class is going to find out about some good health habits.

5. **Student activity.** Ask students to identify one or more habits they would like to change or improve. Ask them to think about why they started the bad habit or why they should improve the existing habit. If they are trying to break a bad habit, what could they do instead? What are some ways to help develop good habits? (1) Post a reminder in a very visible place where you would be doing the new habit. (2) Set a goal, but don't give up if you fail once. Just try again. (3) Reward yourself when you have achieved the goal.

Have students put their resolutions into writing. The record sheet will help them keep track of progress. You may wish to enlist the help of parents to identify habits that need improvement and/or to keep track of progress. Later in the unit you may wish to do this activity again to give students continued support in developing a specific health habit.

6. **Closure.** Reflect on the lesson by asking students whether they think it will be hard or easy to start or change the habit they've chosen. Encourage them to keep at it even though it seems hard.

LESSON 2: KEEPING ACTIVE AND FIT

Preparation/Materials

- For student posters:
  posterboard, one piece per student
  magazines
- Optional: music with a strong beat

Objectives

- Students will recognize that staying active helps them keep physically fit.
- Students will identify specific activities for fitness—and fun.

Background

The last lesson made students aware of their habits and of the importance of good health habits. This and the next lesson deal with the first health habit of the unit—keeping physically fit. Many children in North American society are developing harmful sedentary habits. Hours spent watching television and playing video games are leading to weak and unhealthy bodies. If children learn to keep active while they are young, they will be more likely to stay active throughout life. These lessons encourage students to keep active and stress that all kinds of activities can help keep them physically fit.

Lesson

1. Take the class on a walk to music—either on the playground or in the gymnasium. (If it's necessary to use the classroom, push the desks to one side and have half of the class at a time do the activity). Play the music and have students move various body parts while walking to a strong, regular beat. Tell them to stay in their own space and not to touch others as they move around.

    Or try marching to chants. The leader (the teacher) says one line, and the rest respond. Use the following call, but substitute a class member's name and make up an appropriate rhyme for the second line.

Leader:	I've got a friend her name is *Sue*.
Others:	I've got a friend her name is *Sue*.
Leader:	*She plays the drums and the banjo too.*
Others:	*She plays the drums and the banjo too.*
Leader:	Count off!
Others:	1-2
Leader:	Count off!
Others:	3-4
Leader:	Count off
Others:	1-2-3-4, 1-2-3-4, Let's go!

    -Adapted from the National Dairy Council's *Super You*

    Here are a few examples of substitutions: "I've got a friend his name is Bob/All he eats is corn on the cob"; "I've got a friend her name is Jane/She likes to take long walks in the rain"; "I've got a friend her name is Jill/She gave me a dollar bill." If this seems too difficult or time consuming, use the following chant: "I've got a class that's going to be fit/We'll keep going and never quit."

2. Once the class has returned to the classroom, talk about why the walking or marching activity is good for their bodies. Include the following points in the discussion:
   - Keeping active for long periods of time builds *endurance* (teach the word as vocabulary). Why is endurance important?
   - Being active builds strong muscles (helps us lift and carry things, contributes to good posture).
   - The heart (also a muscle) needs body activity to stay strong (leads to more efficient pumping of blood to muscles and all other parts of the body).
   - Being active is fun. All kinds of activities can help keep fit. They don't have to be boring.

3. Pick up on the last point of the discussion and have students identify things they do for fun that are also helping to keep them active and their bodies fit (for example, walking, roller skating, running games). Encourage them to think of what they do in all four seasons. For this activity you may wish to pair or group students. Then compare lists. Consider making a master list to post in the classroom.

4. **Student activities.** The following activities raise student awareness of ways to develop fitness and the other helps to improve their fitness.
   - Set up a class marathon activity. Choose a particular route (for example, the outer edge of the playground, or gymnasium) and measure the distance. Students can jog the distance or a portion of it once or twice a week. Keep a graph of the distance each student runs to keep interest high.
   - Make posters showing people engaged in various fitness activities. Students can use magazine pictures or draw their own. Have them add an appropriate caption such as "Keep Moving and Stay Fit."

5. **Closure:** "Today we talked about an important health habit—keeping active and fit. By being active we can build strong muscles and build endurance and have fun at the same time. It's one way to take care of the amazing bodies God gave us."

Related Activities

1. Direct the students to keep track of their normal activities for several days. Do active or sedentary activities take up most of their time? Integrate with math and graph the results.

2. Refer to CSI's K-2 Physical Education curriculum for more suggestions for developing fitness. One suggestion is to select a muscle of the week to emphasize in physical education activities. The muscle can be the object of a bulletin board display and can be included in language arts activities.

LESSON 3: ACTIVE ALL BY MYSELF

Preparation/Materials

- Write the poem "Jimmy Jet and His TV Set" on a chart.
- Optional: copy the letter in step 1 onto a sheet of paper.

Objectives

- Students will become aware that watching too much TV is not healthy.
- Students will identify ways to be active when they are alone.

Lesson

1. Read the following letter. To build up interest, copy it onto a sheet of paper and pretend to be surprised when you find it on your desk, or tell the class that the letter came from one of the puppets.

    Dear class,

    I need your help. Please put on your thinking caps and listen to my problem. I'm a TV zombie. As soon as I come home from school, I plop down in front of the TV and stay there until it's time for bed. Well, I do take time out to eat and help clean up the table and take a shower. But the rest of the time I'm glued to the TV.

    You see, there's no one to play with in my neighborhood. And I don't know how to stay active all by myself. Do you have ideas for things I can do to stay fit? I'll be sitting in front of the TV until I hear from you.

2. Have the students brainstorm things a person can do to stay active when alone. Then compose a letter in reply. Student groups can make lists of activities and then work together to write a letter. Or have pairs or groups make the activity lists and then write the letter in full class session. If students compose more than one letter, have groups share their letters with the rest of the class.

    To help students get started, suggest that they think of active things they like to do when they're alone. (Suggestions: jump rope, move to music, make a snowman, play with a foam ball and basketball hoop mounted in doorway, play with a Hula Hoop, ride a bike, work in the yard or house, run a certain distance each day and keep track of the cumulative distance). You may also wish to suggest that the mystery person could ask parents if one or two classmates could come over to play a couple of times a week.

    To keep up the "game," leave the letter(s) in a spot for the mystery person or for the puppet to find. Compose a thank-you letter to read to the class the next day or have Alex or Chris put in an appearance to thank them.

3. Reinforce the lesson concept by reading and talking about the following poem by Shel Silverstein. Put up the chart of the poem so that students can follow along.

Jimmy Jet and His TV Set
I'll tell you the story of Jimmy Jet—
And you know what I tell you is true.
He loved to watch his TV set
Almost as much as you.

He watched all day, he watched all night
Till he grew pale and lean,
From "The Early Show" to "The Late Late Show"
And all the shows between.

He watched till his eyes were frozen wide,
And his bottom grew into his chair.
And his chin turned into a tuning dial,
And antennae grew out of his hair.

And his brains turned into TV tubes,
And his face to a TV screen.
And two knobs saying "VERT." and "HORIZ."
Grew where his ears had been.

And he grew a plug that looked like a tail
So we plugged in little Jim.
And now instead of him watching TV
We all sit around and watch him.

Discuss the poem. Ask students to describe what happened to Jimmy Jet. Explain any lines they don't understand. What do they think the author is trying to say with the poem? How do they feel (physically) after they watch TV for a long time? Conclude that some television watching is fine, but being physically active is better for keeping bodies healthy and strong.

4. **Closure.** Reflect on the lesson with questions such as these:
   * "What are important lessons for staying fit?"
   * "Is staying fit hard for you? Why or why not?"
   * "What can we do to help others stay fit?"

Related Activities

1. Students can illustrate the poem "Jimmy Jet and His TV Set." Consider creating a class booklet of the poem and making an audio recording of the poem available at a center so that students can enjoy the book and recording together.

2. Have students write stories about what the mystery person does when he or she receives their letter(s).

3. Read stories such as Stan and Jan Berenstain's *The Berenstain Bears and Too Much TV* and *When the TV Broke* by Harriet Ziefert.

LESSON 4: EAT FOR FITNESS

Preparation/Materials
- Student Activity
- Chart paper

Objective
- Students will identify why the body needs a variety of foods.

Background
This lesson is the first of four on nutrition, and teachers are encouraged to contact parents by letter explaining topics to be covered and activities planned. You may wish to use this as an opportunity to enlist parents' help with materials for the last lesson and to inquire if any children have allergies to the food you plan to serve.

• •

Lesson

1. Engage students in a discussion of what helps bodies grow (exercise, rest and sleep, and food; heredity also plays a part in how much we grow). Talk about the role of food in helping the body to grow. Ask: "What if you loved watermelon and ate only watermelon for breakfast, lunch, dinner, and snacks everyday? Would that be the best way to help your body grow? Why or why not?" (The body needs a variety of foods. Different foods build up different parts of the body.)

   Brainstorm other reasons (covered in grade 1) for needing a variety of food. Include the following:
   - to give us energy (our fuel to keep our engine running; the more active we are the more energy, or calories, we use; one banana gives enough energy to sleep for an hour and a half but to bicycle for about ten minutes)
   - to keep us healthy (keeps bones and teeth strong, etc.)
   - to prevent sickness (helps bodies fight off germs)

   Make a chart for the classroom of the reasons for a healthy, balanced diet.

2. **Student activity.** Have students cut out and assemble the growing figure in their workbooks. Use tape or fasteners to join the pieces. Show the class how to fold on the dotted lines and then gradually unfold the paper doll to make it grow.

3. **Closure.** Summarize the lesson by reading what is written on the figures. Close by praising and thanking God for the daily provision of food. Consider singing songs such as "Praise and Thanksgiving Let Everyone Bring" (*Children's Hymnal,* 48).

LESSON 5: CLASSIFYING FOOD

Preparation/Materials

- Pictures of foods for reviewing the food groups (at least three pictures for each main food group and pictures of foods from the extras group and from the combination group—such as tacos or pizza)
- Seven boxes or bags for sorting food pictures. Label each with the name of a food category: dairy, proteins, fruits, vegetables, grains, extras, and combination.
- Materials for footprints game:
  poster board
  pictures of food
  clear adhesive paper (Contact paper)
  recorded or live music
  Cut footprints from poster board. Then on each footprint glue a picture of a food. Laminate the footprints or cover the footprints with clear Contact paper. Make one footprint for each student taking part in the game. Make a list of the foods appearing on the footprints for easy reference.

Objectives

- Students will review the food groups.
- Students will identify the amounts needed daily from each food group for a balanced diet.

Background

Years ago, after assessing the daily dietary needs of most people, the United States Department of Agriculture formulated a food pyramid which included the eating of all types of foods. The food pyramid was redesigned in 2005. In 2010 the information from MyPyramid was redesigned to MyPlate. Suggestions for healthy eating were slightly modified. These foods are considered beneficial to the growth and development of healthy bodies. MyPlate is divided into five categories: grains, vegetables, fruits, dairy products, and proteins. Oils are not considered a food group, but they are essential for good health. Solid fats and added sugars are called empty calories. The food groups are organized according to proportions needed each day in order to provide the body with the right amount of nutrients.

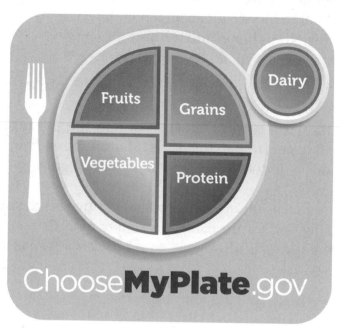

Lesson

1. Briefly review the reasons for eating food and the necessity for eating a variety of foods. Recall that the nutrients our bodies need come from five main types or groups of food (the five food groups are taught in grade 1).

2. Use the pictures to review the food groups. Have students take turns choosing a picture of a food and placing it in the correct food group box or bag. Have the rest of the class vote on whether they agree with the chosen classification. Recall how each of the groups helps us stay healthy: the dairy group makes teeth and bones strong, proteins build muscles and bones and skin, fruits and vegetables affect night vision and healing of cuts, and the grain group provides energy.

   Explain the "extras" category. Note that these foods contain little to keep us growing and healthy, and are high in sugar and fats. Show students the pictures of foods in this category and have them put the pictures in the correct container.

   The following are recommended daily servings for second graders from each of the five food groups (these are minimum amounts):
       5 ozs. from the grains group
       2 cups from the vegetables group
       1 ½ cups from the fruits group
       2 cups from the dairy group
       5 ozs. from the proteins group

   Write these numbers clearly on the group containers. Point out that there is no serving requirement for the extras category because extras don't have enough nutrients to keep our bodies healthy, and if we eat too many extras, our bodies will be less healthy.

   Finally discuss the pictures of combination foods. Explain that these foods represent more than one food group. Have students identify the various food groups found in each combination food.

3. Play musical footprints (similar to musical chairs). Arrange the prepared footprints in a large circle on the floor, play music, and have students walk around the circle stepping on the footprints. Stop the music and name a food that appears on one of the footprints. The student standing on that print identifies what food group it belongs to. (If this is difficult for students, list the names of the food groups on the board as a help.) Remove the footprint and the student leaves the game. Continue the game until one person and one food footprint remains. This person can be the leader of the next game and call out the food names.

4. **Closure:** "We talked about how many servings we need from each of the food groups each day. (Briefly review.) Why isn't it healthy to eat too many foods from the extras group? Why do you think we sometimes call those foods 'junk food'?"

● ●

Related Activities

1. Have students make posters depicting the five food groups. Instruct them to divide a sheet of construction paper into five sections and label the sections "Dairy Group," "Protein Group," "Fruit Group," "Vegetable Group," and "Grain Group." Then they should draw or cut out of magazines pictures that belong in each of the food groups. If you wish to make this a group activity, have groups of five work together to make large posters, with each member of the group contributing the pictures for one food group. Have them make a heading for each food group stating the minimum number of daily servings.

2. Center idea: make a matching memory game to help students classify foods. Make two sets of cards, one with names of the five food groups and one with pictures of foods. The food group set consists of ten cards with the name of each food group appearing on two cards. The food set (also ten cards), pictures two different foods from each of the five food groups.

   Students place shuffled cards face down in rows (four rows of five cards). Players take turns turning over two cards at a time. If a player turns over a set—a food card and its matching food group, he or she picks up the cards. The turn continues as long as the player's chosen pair of cards match. Unmatched cards are put back in their original spots, face down.

   To keep score, count up the number of matched pairs each players has. The one with the most matched pairs wins.

3. Explore what types of food are eaten in other cultures or countries. Integrate with current social studies or perhaps tie in with various ethnic backgrounds represented in the class. Consider asking parents to bring in specialties for the class to sample.

LESSON 6: KEEPING IN BALANCE

Preparation/Materials
- For student activity:
  art materials
  paper plates, one per student

Objective
- Students will apply knowledge of food groups and daily minimum requirements to plan a balanced daily menu.

Background
The major issue in nutrition for most students is not scarcity of foods from each of the four food groups, but making the right choices from among the wide range of foods available to them. Of course, at this age most students are dependent on the choices of their adult caregivers; nevertheless, they can choose whether or not to eat the foods the adults provide, and they often choose some of their snacks.

Lesson

1. Draw a blank MyPlate on the board. Ask the students to name the five food groups. The students should give examples from each. Example: protein–beans, steak, pork.

2. Have each student plan a day's menu. Follow these steps:
   - Direct students to write down the names of food groups at the top of a sheet of paper. Then list an appropriate number of choices under each grouping. (For example, fruit: orange juice, banana, apple, kiwi.)
   - On a second sheet of paper have them write the headings Breakfast, Lunch, Dinner, Snack. Then direct them to write under each heading what they would choose to eat for each of those meals. The catch is that they must plan a balanced day's diet with sufficient servings from each of the groups. They can refer to the listings of food group names and choices for help. Extras can be included, but they must be in moderate amounts.
   - Have pairs of students share their work and check on whether their partner's choices "add" up to a balanced menu.

3. **Student activity**. Give students opportunity to "produce" one of the meals on their menu. They can draw, color, and cut out the food items and paste them on a paper plate. If time permits, have students share their "meals." What other foods must be added to make up the day's quotas?

4. **Closure:** "Today we used what we know about food groups to plan healthy meals for one day. Tomorrow we'll be planning a breakfast menu."

Related Activities

1. Center idea: Have sets of food cards available for students to use to plan balanced menus or to sort into food groups. These can be pictures or printed flash cards made by cutting labels from grocery cans and boxes.

   Consider setting the center up like a market. Include a supply of lunch bags at the center. The students can go grocery shopping to pick out the appropriate number from each group and place them in a bag. The "cashier" can check the purchases to be sure that the right number has been included.

2. Roleplay or use puppets to present situations having to do with making food choices. Situations to discuss: facing "strange" food at a friend's house or disliked food at home, choosing snacks.

3. Read stories and poems about food. Here are a few poetry suggestions, all from the *Random House Book of Poetry for Children:*
   "Twickham Tweer" by Jack Prelutsky
   "Chocolate Chocolate" and "My Mouth" by
       Arnold Adoff
   "Pie Problem" by Shel Silverstein
   "Egg Thoughts" by Russell Hoban
   "Oodles of Noodles" by Lucia and James L.
       Hymes, Jr.

LESSON 7: BREAKING THE FAST

Preparation/Materials
- Student Activities 1 and 2

Objectives
- Students will become aware of the importance of eating breakfast.
- Students will identify how breakfasts can contribute to daily requirements from food groups.

Background

Breakfast is an important meal. Research shows that people who eat breakfast are better able to concentrate, can react more quickly, and tire less easily than those who skip breakfast. Breakfast helps to give us the energy to get going.

Skipping breakfast also makes it harder to meet the body's nutritional needs. A breakfast should consist of food from at least three of the five food groups. It should supply about one-fourth of the daily nutrients. Sometimes people skip breakfast because they are tired of traditional breakfast foods or simply don't like them. Less conventional breakfast, however, can be just as nutritious.

This lesson is adapted from the National Dairy Council's program *Food … Gives Me Energy*.

Lesson

1. Write the word *breakfast* on the board. Explain what a "fast" is. Write *break the fast* on the board, and tell students that's what we're doing when we have breakfast. Since we don't eat while we're sleeping, we're fasting. When we wake up, we're hungry.

2. Discuss reasons—besides hunger—for eating breakfast (to give energy, to provide some of daily nutrition requirements, to enjoy the taste of food). Then tell students one of your favorite breakfast foods, and let them each name one of theirs (and perhaps identify its food group).

   A common excuse for skipping breakfast is the lack of time. Breakfast doesn't have to take a lot of time to prepare or eat. A sandwich can be prepared the night before and eaten with a glass of fruit juice. While not traditionally considered a breakfast menu, this choice still is drawn from the five food groups and provides the needed energy.

   Ask if any class members ever skip breakfast. How do they feel when they don't have breakfast? Explain that when people don't eat breakfast, they often feel hungry later in the morning and sometimes tired, too. Stress that everyone should eat something in the morning, but a breakfast doesn't have to be big. Even a piece of fruit eaten on the way to school is better than going without.

3. **Student activity.** Tell the class to pretend that the classroom is a restaurant and that they are going to have breakfast in the restaurant. Introduce Student Activity 1 — the restaurant menu.

- Go over the menu with the students, naming and reading the items offered for each breakfast choice. Teach new vocabulary as necessary.
- Then go over the menu again. This time have students identify the food group of each item. Ask if breakfast 1 has anything in it from the fruit group (orange juice), vegetable group (no), protein group (no), dairy group (cheese), and grain group (crackers). Choose a color to represent each food group (for example, blue for dairy, red for protein; green for vegetable; orange for fruit, and brown for grain), and ask students to circle each food in breakfast 1 to show the food group to which it belongs. Use this procedure to work through all the breakfast choices on the menu.
- Discuss the menus. Lead students to identify which of the breakfasts has foods from all five food groups and which ones do not. Stress that all of these breakfasts will give energy and all have food from at least three groups.
- Choose one of the breakfasts and have students subtract its number of servings from the daily required number of servings. Discuss how the remaining amounts could be met by snacks, lunch, and dinner.
- Ask students which of the menus they like the best. Have them indicate their choices on the activity sheet. If you wish, make a graph of the class members' choices.

4. **Student activity.** Explain that students are going to make their own breakfast menu. Turn to Activity Sheet 2 and have students write down their choices for each food group. Then give them time to draw a picture of the breakfast. Students can also name their restaurants.

5. **Closure.** Praise students for their skill in planning their restaurant menus, and encourage them to eat breakfast each day so that they'll have energy.

• •

Related Activities

1. Keep a class breakfast record. For two or three days chart the foods the class (and teacher) eat for breakfast. Encourage students to truthfully say what they ate and record them without comment. When the chart is completed, look at the results. What food is most commonly eaten? Least commonly? If there are unusual foods on the list, point out that every family has different eating habits. Identify the different food groups to which the foods belong.

2. What breakfasts are common in different cultures? (For example, Japanese eat rice, fish, and seaweed for breakfast.) Students from various ethnic backgrounds can talk about their eating habits.

LESSON 8: BUILDING BREAKFAST IN A BOWL

Preparation/Materials
- Have students wash their hands and classroom tables just before the lesson.
- Arrange for preparing ingredients and obtaining necessary equipment for serving (enlist help of parents).
- Ingredients for "breakfast in a bowl":
  yogurt (plan about three servings from each 8 ounce container)
  fruit, cut up or sliced (apples, bananas, berries, pineapple, or other seasonal fruit, or a choice of fruit)
  granola or similar type unsweetened cereal, 1-2 boxes
- Serving utensils:
  serving bowls, two for each ingredient (to speed serving)
  at least six serving spoons
  paper bowls or cups, one per student
  spoons, one per student
  napkins, one per student
- Student Activity

Objectives
- Students will review health rules for handling food.
- Students will review unit concepts about food groups and nutrition requirements.
- Students will apply what they have learned and build a healthy breakfast.

Background
This lesson follows up on the previous lesson and gives students the opportunity to build a simple but healthy breakfast. Students used to eggs and toast may find this breakfast unfamiliar, but stress that the important thing is to eat a nutritious breakfast.

Lesson
1. Tell students that they are going to make a good breakfast in one bowl. An alternate option is a breakfast consisting of graham crackers spread with peanut butter and topped with a slice or two of banana. If accompanied with a drink of milk, this breakfast contains four of the five food groups.

2. Check over basic rules for clean food preparation before you begin:
   - wash hands and table(s)
   - "drop" control—throw away food that drops on the floor and wash utensils that drop on the floor
   - sneeze control—cover mouth and nose or turn away from food

3. Have students help with the preparation as much as possible. Ask volunteers to set out plates, napkins, and spoons. Although it will save class time if the fruit is washed and cut up ahead of time, consider enlisting students to wash fruit and, if possible, slice or chop it using serrated plastic knives.

4. Make your own "breakfast in a bowl" to demonstrate the procedure. Identify each of the ingredients and list them on the board. People often start out with yogurt, add granola, and top it off with fruit, but, of course, students can put the ingredients together in any order they prefer. Ask: "Do you think this breakfast would be enough for you in the morning? Why or why not?"

5. Hand out the activity sheet and explain that while students are waiting their turn to make breakfast, they can complete the worksheet. First, students should decide to what food group each of the "breakfast in a bowl" ingredients belongs to (refer them to the list on the board). Next, have them draw a picture of each ingredient on the activity sheet—in the correct space. For example, since yogurt belongs to the dairy group, students should draw a bowl of yogurt in the space labeled "Dairy Group" on the activity sheet. (You may wish to warn them that all food groups are not represented in "breakfast in a bowl.") Then ask them to draw a picture of themselves doing something that uses a lot of energy.

6. Let class members take turns building their yogurt specials. Those served first can work on the activity sheet and wait to eat until everyone has been served.

7. **Closure.** Use the completed activity sheets to discuss the nutrients in the breakfast. Ask students why this breakfast will give them energy, what food groups are represented, and what they could eat later in the day to meet requirements from the groups (protein and vegetable) that are not represented.

LESSON 9: TIME OUT FOR SLEEP

Preparation/Materials
- Health puppets
- Plan puppet script.
- Story about sleep to read to the class

Objectives
- Students will become aware of the effects of lack of sleep.
- Students will understand that they need sufficient rest in order to function well.

Lesson

1. Use Alex and Chris to introduce the health habit highlighted in this lesson—getting enough sleep. Have one puppet complaining about being tired. Then have the second puppet come bouncing along energetically, full of ideas for active games:

   Alex: Wow! What a long day.

   Chris: Hiya! Wanna play a game of catch?

   Alex: No, I don't think so.

   Chris: Well, why don't we have a race? I'll race you to the corner. The one who wins gets to pick what we'll do next.

   Alex: No, I don't want to run.

   Chris: Hey, what's the matter?

   Have Alex explain that he is really tired from staying up late the night before. Continue the conversation or comment on it to make the following points:
   - Lack of sleep affects performance during the day. It may keep us from doing good work at school and from having energy to play and to have fun.
   - Lack of sleep may make us feel tired and cranky.
   - Everyone needs a good night's rest, but some people need more sleep than others.

2. **Discussion.** Explain that sleep is a mystery. No one knows exactly why we need sleep, but sleep appears to be important for the brain. Our brain needs time to relax and to recharge. Our sleep is regulated by our built-in body clock. (The pineal gland secretes melatonin during the hours of darkness but stops during the day.) Nobody knows exactly how body clocks work. Plants and animals have body clocks, too.

   Ask students how much sleep they think they need. (Children their age need about 10 or 11 hours of sleep.) Talk about how much sleep babies need (about half of the day). Note that most people need less sleep as they grow older. Part of the sleep time is dream-type sleep. We dream every night whether we remember it or not. On average we dream about five or six times a night.

3. Read a selection from children's literature about sleep. A good choice is Paul Showers' *Sleep Is for Everyone,* which explores what is happening in our bodies while we're

sleeping and why some people need more sleep than others. Other titles about going to bed or about sleeping:

Good Night Everyone! and *I Won't Go to Bed!* by Harriet Ziefert

The Dream Child by David McPhail

While You Are Asleep by Gwynne L. Isaacs (for grades 4-8, but some sections may be suitable)

4. **Writing activity.** Based on the discussion, ask students to write a short paragraph on the topic of sleep. Provide story starters such as the following.

   • I need sleep because …

   • I know I don't get enough sleep when …

   • When I go to bed, I …

   Write additional story starters to fit with the book you read with the class.

   To add interest, provide students with a construction paper pillows (or bed or comforter) on which to write their paragraphs. Use the finished "pillows" to create a bulletin board display. (Add a caption such as "Sleep Is for Everyone" or "Sleep Well, Be Well.")

5. **Closure:** "Today we learned that God made each of us with a body clock. Our body clock sees to it that we sleep at night. Why is important to get enough sleep?" (Refer to list in step 1.)

• •

Related Activities

1. Have students keep track of the number of hours they sleep for three or four nights. Do they think they are getting enough sleep? Why or why not?

2. Integrate with science by studying the day and night cycle.

3. Integrate with language arts by having students write stories about an imaginary child who never slept or write descriptions of their own bedtime routine. Consider reading poems about going to bed as an introduction to the activity. Some suggested poems: "Going to Bed" by Marchette Chute, "Bedtime" by Elanor Farjeon, or "Charlie's Bedtime" by Lee Bennett Hopkins in *Go to Bed! A Book of Bedtime Poems.*

LESSON 10: PERSONAL GROOMING AND HEALTH

Preparation/Materials
- Student Activity
- Write grooming habits on slips of paper, one for each group of students to act out.

Objectives
- Students will identify basic good grooming habits.
- Students will describe how good grooming contributes to health.

Background
The origin of health education is personal health. In the early years of school health programs, personal health was the entire curriculum. However, more recently the trend has been to de-emphasize personal health. One reason is that most of the major contagious illnesses associated with personal health habits have either been eradicated or controlled.

However, this trend to de-emphasize personal health as a topic in health education is unfortunate. Take the mundane area of dental health, for example. Fully 97 percent of the students in our schools will have some kind of dental problems in their lifetime. Reminders about daily personal health habits may seem to be a form of parental or teacher nagging, but students do need to be reminded that they can spread germs when they do not wash their hands before they eat or after they use the bathroom. Stress the positive side of personal health. Grooming habits such as bathing and brushing teeth and hair will help students stay healthy and clean and be more attractive. And they will like themselves better when they are well-groomed and clean.

• •

Lesson

1. Teach students the word *grooming*. Tell them that good health habits include good grooming habits.

2. Have students pantomime personal health habits—shampooing and combing/brushing hair, washing hands after playing or before eating, scrubbing/trimming fingernails, taking a shower, putting on clean clothes, brushing/flossing teeth. Divide the class into groups and give each group a slip of paper naming the grooming habit they are to present.

   After each group presents its pantomime, have the rest of the class identify what it is. Then ask the class to tell how the habit contributes to good health.

3. **Student activity.** Students can fill in the blanks and complete the crossword puzzle. Answers: Across (1) healthy, (2) nails, (3) wash (4) germs; Down (1) habit, (2) hair, (3) shower, (4) brush. Then have them solve the riddle. Riddle answer: soap.

4. **Closure.** Summarize the value of good grooming. Points to stress: washing off dirt equals washing away germs that can make us sick; feeling good on the outside can help you feel good on the inside; clean bodies are more attractive; God gives us the responsibility for taking care of our bodies.

• •

Related Activities

1. Integrate with math. Have the children bring in the labels from the type of bar soap they use at home. Graph the different types by gluing the labels in columns on a chart.

2. Have the children collect and donate personal grooming aids for a mission cause. As the donations are brought in sort, count, and graph the donations.

3. Center idea: tie in with Unit 2 on the family by identifying items the family provides for personal grooming: toothbrushes and toothpaste, shampoo and soap, combs and brushes, washclothes, towels, warm water, electricity or gas for water heaters. Students can cut pictures of the items out of magazines to make posters.

LESSON 11: BRUSHING AND FLOSSING

Preparation/Materials
- Student Visual
- Toothbrush and dental floss for demonstration
- White tempera paint
- Yarn, an 18-inch piece for each pair of students
- Student Activity
- Optional: student dental kits with disclosing agents and toothbrushes, one per student
- Optional: small mirrors, one for every pair of students
- Optional: invite a dental hygienist or other professional to speak to the class about dental care.

Objectives
- Students will be able to define plaque.
- Students will review toothbrushing techniques.
- Students will be introduced to flossing.

Background
Three primary teeth of the average six-year-old child have been attacked by decay at least once. And by age 21, the average adult has 11 decayed, missing, or filled teeth. So neglecting daily personal oral care during youth has severe effects. The chief problem in children's oral health is dental caries—cavities.

What causes dental caries? The American Dental Association explains that a dental cavity is not just a hole in a tooth. Rather, it is the result of a bacterial infection. Plaque, "a soft, sticky, colorless layer of bacteria" that is constantly forming, sticks to the teeth. Then when the person eats a food containing sugar, the bacteria break down the food and change the sugar to acid. After repeated acid attacks, the tooth's enamel is penetrated, bacteria enter the tooth, and a cavity results.

Reducing sugar and starch in the diet is one way of reducing cavities. But the problem is not just the amount of sugar or starch. The Dental Association stresses that frequency of eating sugar-rich food, the length of time the sugar stays in the mouth, and the physical form of the food (such as sticky sweets) are all important factors in producing cavities.

Of course, another way to reduce cavities is to remove the plaque by brushing and flossing. One of the best ways to educate children about plaque is to use a disclosing solution (a harmless vegetable dye), so that they can actually see the plaque on their teeth.

Valuable resources for these lessons are local dentists, hygienists, or community groups interested in school health education. They may be able to provide a model for demonstrating tooth cleaning techniques and other helpful materials.

If dental kits with disclosing agents and toothbrushes are available, you may wish to arrange for the class to use the disclosing agent, brush teeth, and then use the disclosing agent once more. If this is not feasible at school, have students do this at home with parents supervising and then have them report on the experience.

Lesson
1. Review daily health habits covered so far in this unit. Have students identify a daily health care habit that has to do with the mouth (tooth care). Ask what they do to take care of their teeth. (Most will say that they brush their teeth; some may also floss.) Ask:

"Why do we need teeth?" (For attractive appearance, for eating food, for talking — demonstrate with *s* and *th* sounds.)

2. Refer students to the visual of plaque in their workbooks. Explain that when they clean their teeth they are removing plaque. Tell students that plaque is a soft, sticky, colorless layer of bacteria (or germs) that everyone gets on their teeth. Plaque is constantly being formed. If the plaque stays on their teeth, it will harden (into calculus). The best way to remove plaque is by brushing and flossing.

3. Show the toothbrush and dental floss and discuss how these are used to remove plaque. (If necessary, review toothbrushing techniques with the class. Explain the need for flossing by pointing out on the visual how plaque gets on the sides of the teeth where it's hard to get at it with a toothbrush. Flossing helps to remove plaque in those areas.

4. If dental kits are available, have students use the disclosing agents and mirrors to see the plaque on their teeth.

5. Introduce dental flossing. Teaching actual flossing in class should not be attempted at this grade level without the assistance of a dental professional. The American Dental Association suggests introducing the idea of flossing with the following demonstration and activity:
   - Cover your hand with thick tempera paint. Then use a toothbrush to clean off the paint, holding fingers tightly together. The brush will not remove material from between the fingers. Then make a comparison with plaque between the teeth.
   - Give each child a piece of yarn 18 inches long. Have children get a partner and practice flossing by using yarn and the partner's hand. One student holds out a hand with fingers straight and held tightly together. The other student flosses between the fingers.

   Note: the American Dental Association stresses that preschool-grade 3 instruction in flossing should center on removing plaque without injuring gums. Students should not snap the floss into place.

6. Lead students to identify a third component of good tooth care—regular visits to a dentist. Ask: "Why is this important? What does the dentist do?" (See if our teeth are growing right and check for cavities.)

7. **Student activity.** To encourage good dental habits have students keep track of their brushing and flossing for two weeks. Refer to the plaque control charts in the student workbook which class members are to take home. Explain the purpose of the charts. After the charts are returned to school, acknowledge successful completion with a certificate or with a sample-size tube of toothpaste for each participant, or with a class treat—of healthy snacks.

8. **Closure.** Summarize and evaluate with questions such as the following:
   - "What is plaque?"
   - "How can we get rid of plaque?"
   - "Why should we floss as well as brush our teeth?"
   - "Why is it important to visit the dentist regularly?"
   - "Will it be hard for you to bring the chart back full of smiling faces? Why or why not?"

• •

Related Activities

- Show the American Dental Association film
  It's Dental Flossopophy, Charlie Brown.

LESSON 12: SMART SNACKS FOR TEETH

Preparation/Materials

- Student Activity
- Optional: index cards, one per student
- Optional: construction paper, one sheet per student

Objectives

- Students will become aware of the role of food in dental health.
- Students will identify healthful snacks.

• •

Lesson

1. Ask students to recall ways to take care of teeth (toothbrushing and flossing to remove plaque). Ask them if they can think of another way to take care of their teeth. Lead them to conclude that sugar or sweet, sticky foods are not good for teeth. Explain that the bacteria in plaque changes sugar into acid which, in turn, attacks the tooth (enamel) and makes a hole or cavity. We call these foods trigger foods because each time we eat sugar we "trigger" an acid attack that lasts about 20 minutes.

2. Make a list of snacks with the class. Without comment write down all their suggestions on the board. Then go over the list and ask the class to vote on whether a snack is good or not so good for their teeth. (Suggestion: give children index cards and have them draw a happy face on one side and sad face on the other side. They can use the cards to vote.) Talk about why a snack is healthy or not so healthy.

3. Brainstorm a new list of snacks. This time include only "smart" snacks. Things to include: popcorn, pretzels, cheese, crackers, nuts, sunflower seeds, fruits, raw vegetables, milk, unsweetened fruit juices.

4. Have students copy the list to take home and post in a prominent place. If time permits, consider having them paste the list on a piece of construction paper and add illustrations or slogans.

   Alternate option: have students make a class booklet of smart snacks. Each child could make one page picturing a smart snack. Make this a center activity and put the completed book in the library for students to enjoy or let students take it home by turns.

5. **Student activity/unit review.** Use the worksheet to review unit concepts. Have students give advice to Chris and Alex. If this is difficult for your class, discuss and solve the problems in full class session. Students can write in their answers after the class agrees on what advice to give. (You may also wish to use the activity to teach cause and effect.) The riddle answer: heart.

6. **Closure.** End the unit by talking with students about why it's important to take care of our bodies. Stress that God created our bodies and we should treat them with respect.

● ●

Related Activities

1. Close the unit the way it began—with Alex and/or Chris telling the class about their daily routine. Have them include both good and bad habits. Break out of role to interact with students. Ask them to identify whether the habits are good or bad. And ask them to explain the purpose of the good habits.

2. Use the Unit 5, Lesson 1 Student Activity to reinforce the idea that students have the responsibility to take care of their bodies. Check up on their efforts to substitute good habits for bad. You may wish to do the activity one more time and have class members focus on changing a different habit.

3. Write a story about someone who didn't have good personal health habits. Encourage students to write a tall tale that exaggerates descriptions and incidents for humorous effect.

4. Use "My Health," Part 3 of the American Cancer Society's kit *An Early Start to Good Health.* The filmstrip "The Adventures of Healthman" is a mini-musical about a Superman look-alike and focuses on choosing good health habits.

Unit 6

Keeping Safe

Goals

- Students will become aware of potential safety hazards.
- Students will choose to obey safety rules.
- Students will develop skills and strategies for self-protection.

Background

This unit covers several basic safety issues — traffic safety, fire safety, and stranger and child abuse education. The first two are straightforward safety issues. We all recognize that children must be aware of potential traffic and fire hazards and need to develop skills to protect themselves. But the last two areas — stranger and child abuse education—are also basic safety issues; students need help in those areas also. As much as we would like young children to remain innocent, in order to protect children we must deal with the reality of danger and of sinful acts such as child abuse. Of course, it's important to take a balanced approach. Students must be informed, but care should be taken not to unnecessarily frighten them. Be matter-of-fact, and encourage them to develop self-confidence in dealing with all these issues.

Vocabulary

Integrate the following vocabulary:

safety	bedroom	cords	stranger	living room
accident	kitchen	secret	smoke	private parts
warning	danger	escape	plugs	confusing
caution	hall	poison	touch	

Unit Resources

Davis, Diane. *Something Is Wrong At My House: A Book About Parent Fighting*. Seattle: Parenting Press, 1984.

Winston-Hillier, Randy. *Some Secrets Are for Sharing*. Denver: MAC, 1986.
> Both of these books deal with domestic violence. Davis's book addresses the problem of violent parental fights; Winston-Hillier's book addresses the problem of emotional and physical abuse of a child by a parent. These problems are not covered in the health program, but teachers may wish to use these resources one-on-one with students living with family violence.

Mr. Know-It-Owl's Safety Tips. Videocassette. Apollo.
> Segments include "Emergencies," "What Would You Do?" "Roscoe's Rules and Electrical Safety: A to Zap." Available from KIMBO, Dept. 8, P.O. Box 477, Long Branch, New Jersey 07740-0477; phone 800-631-2187.

KidsRights is a comprehensive source/distributor for materials on personal safety issues.
> For a catalog, contact KidsRights, 3700 Progress Boulevard, Mount Dora, Florida, 32757; phone 800-892-KIDS.

Safety Stories Series. Filmstrips. Encyclopedia Britannica, 1980.

Lesson Resources

Lesson 1

Hall, Barbara and Doug. *Playing It Safe: Home, Summer, and Winter Street Smart Activities for Children.* Willowdale, Ont.: Firefly Books, 1990.

> Endorsed by the Block Parent Program of Canada, this activity book (intended for ages 5-10) illustrates a variety of safety rules. Pages are reproducible for classroom instruction. Useful for both Lessons 1 and 2.

Skidmore, Steve. *Poison! Beware! Be an Expert Poison Spotter.* Brookfield, Conn.: Millbrook Press, 1991.

> Detailed information about poison in the everyday environment.

Lesson 2

Blakely, Cindy, and Suzanne Drinkwater. *The Look Out! Book: A Child's Guide to Street Safety.* Toronto/New York: Scholastic, 1986.

Brown, Marc, and Stephen Krensky. *Dinosaurs Beware! A Safety Guide.* Boston: Little, Brown, 1984.

> Direct safety statements combined with zany illustrations.

Bucklebear Team's Traffic Safety Series. Okemos, Mich.: Shinn.

> This resource includes material on car passenger safety and pedestrian safety. Teacher guides, videos, activity books, color books, posters, and stickers are available. Items can be bought separately. Order from Shinn & Associates, 2853 W. Jolly St., Okemos, Michigan 48864; phone 517-332-0211.

Chlad, Dorothy. *When I Cross the Street.* Chicago: Childrens Press, 1982.

Otto the Auto. 16mm film or VHS Videocassette. Washington, D.C.: AAA Foundation for Traffic Safety, 1957-1981.

> These are six, single-concept cartoon films for primary grade level. Otto is an animated car that teaches pedestrian, passenger, and bicycle safety education. Contact the local AAA office for this resource or for a catalog of available materials or contact AAA Foundation for Traffic Safety, 1730 M Street, NW, Suite 401, Washington, D.C. 20036; phone 202-775-1456.

Safety Belt Activity Book. Washington, D.C.: National Highway Traffic Safety Administration, 1977.

> This booklet for grades K-6 is available from the National Highway Traffic Safety Administration, Office of Occupant Protection, NTS-13, 400 Seventh St. SW, Washington, D.C. 20590; phone 202-366-1755. Other materials such as pamphlets, posters, and coloring books are also available. Most materials are free of charge and reproducible. A catalog is available.

See and Be Seen. Videocassette or 16mm film. Washington, D.C.: AAA Foundation for Traffic Safety, 1988.

> A 9-minute film for children 5-7 years old that teaches safe street crossing techniques.

Walk Safely. Videocassette. Fiesta Films.

> Based on extensive data of children's street-crossing behavior, this 13-minute film illustrates the most frequent dangerous situations.

Lesson 3

Buschman, Janis, and Debbie Hunley. *Strangers Don't Look Like the Big Bad Wolf!* Children's Safety Series, Book 5. Edmonds, Wash.: Franklin Press, 1985.

Campbell, Louisa. *Ernie Gets Lost.* New York: Western Publishing, 1985.
   This Sesame Street book for grades K-3 is also available in audiocassette.

Chlad, Dorothy. *Strangers.* Chicago: Childrens Press, 1982.

Girard, Linda Walvoord. *Who Is a Stranger and What Should I Do?* Niles, Ill.: Whitman, 1985.
   A well-written book with a balanced approach.

Holland, M., and J. Demers. *How Do You Know Who's a Stranger?* Pinellas Park, Fla.: Willowisp, 1987.

Lenett, Robin, and Dana Barthelme with Bob Crause. *Sometimes It's O.K. to Tell Secrets! A Parent/Child Manual for Protection of Children.* New York: Tom Doherty Association, 1986.

Too Smart for Strangers. Videocassette. Walt Disney.
   Intended for ages 3-10, this 40-minute film teaches children to say no to strangers who approach them, quickly get away, and report to an adult.

Lesson 4

Chlad, Dorothy. *Matches, Lighters, and Firecrackers Are Not Toys.* Chicago: Childrens Press, 1982.

Learn Not to Burn Curriculum: A Fire Prevention and Safety Education Program for School Children, Level 1. Third edition. Quincy, Mass.: National Fire Protection Association, 1987.
   Contains 22 lesson plans, lists of teaching aids, and fire safety information for teachers. The Learn Not to Burn program is being used in both Canadian and U.S. schools. For more information contact the Canadian Fire Safety Association, 2175 Sheppard Ave., E., Willowdale, Ontario M2J 1W8, the U.S. headquarters (address below), or your local branch.

The U.S. National Fire Protection Association has a wealth of materials available: videos and filmstrips, activity and coloring books, stickers and posters. For a catalog, contact the association at 1 Batterymarch Park, Quincy, Massachusetts 02269-9101; phone 800-344-3555.

Smoke Detectives. Kits. Chicago: State Farm Insurance.
   Year-round multidisciplinary safety program for K-6 classrooms. To order contact Smoke Detectives, P.O. Box 3252, Chicago, Illinois 60654.

What Do I Do When I See a Fire? Film. Quincy, Mass.: National Fire Protection Agency.
   Puppets teach about how to report a fire.

Lesson 5

Bahr, Amy. *It's Okay to Say No.* New York: Grosset & Dunlap, 1986.

C.A.R.E. Kit: A Sexual Abuse Prevention Program for Children Aged 5-9. Surrey, B.C.: Child Abuse Education Productions Association.
   A comprehensive, but rather costly resource, which includes a teacher guide with lesson plans, visuals for presenting key ideas, audiocassette and student book, and puppets. Write to the publisher: P.O. Box 183, Surrey, British Columbia V3T 4W8; phone 604-581-5116.

Carl, Angela R. *Good Hugs and Bad Hugs*. Cincinnati, Ohio: Standard, 1985.
This activity book is a helpful teacher resource providing activities for reinforcing or expanding lesson ideas. Written from a Christian perspective, the level of individual activities varies considerably.

Colao, Flora, and Tamar Hosansky. *Your Children Should Know*. New York: Harper, 1983.
A teacher resource providing information on the reasons for abuse and ways to prevent abuse.

Dayee, Frances S. *Private Zone*. New York: Warner Books, 1982.
A read-together book about appropriate/inappropriate touching that avoids naming anatomical parts and instead uses the term "private zone." It defines the private zone as special parts of the body covered by a bathing suit. Simple and clear presentation of basics for preventing sexual abuse.

De Moor, Ary, and others. *Child Abuse Education*. Part 3 of *Now You Are the Body of Christ: A Family Life Education Program for Christian Schools*. Edmonton: CSI District 11 Association/Grand Rapids: Christian Schools International, 1989.
Developed by the Curriculum Coordinator and five teachers of CSI District 11, this is a curriculum outline for teaching abuse prevention in kindergarten through grade 12. This valuable resource includes a sample protocol for reporting sexual abuse. Order from District 11 Curriculum Office, The King's College, 10766 - 97th Street, Edmonton, Alberta T4H 2M1 or from Christian Schools International.

Freeman, Lory. *It's My Body*. Seattle: Parenting Press, 1982.
Intended to help children ages 3-6 identify uncomfortable touch, the book gives them the language to deal with "unwanted touching of any kind."

Girard, Linda Walvoord. *My Body Is Private*. Niles, Ill.: Whitman, 1984.
Sensitively written book that covers types of touches, dealing with disturbing situations, and telling adults about inappropriate touch. For ages 5-8.

Jance, Judith. *It's Not Your Fault*. Children's Safety Series. Edmonds, Wash.: Charles Franklin Press, 1985.
Including a read-aloud section, discussion questions, and background information, Jance's helpful book has two purposes—to assure children who have been sexually abused that they are not responsible and to teach all children the basics of preventing sexual abuse. The read-aloud story is about Terry and how she comes to tell adults about the sexual abuse by her step-grandfather. For ages 6-10.

Kehoe, Patricia. *Something Happened and I'm Scared to Tell: A Book for Young Victims of Abuse*. Seattle: Parenting Press, 1987.
Intended for the young child between 3 and 7 who is a suspected victim of sexual or physical abuse, this 26-page booklet is designed to encourage victims to speak out. Summary: in conversation with a kind lion, a child tells about being abused. The lion encourages the child to tell the truth and keep on telling the truth until somebody listens, names people who may be abusers (including some family members), defines sexual abuse (naming genitals—vagina, penis, and anus), and helps the child recognize and deal with confused feelings. A direct, honest, and supportive approach.

Kraizer, Sherryll Kerns. *The Safe Child Book.* New York: Delacorte, 1985.
> This book is intended for parents, but teachers will also find it helpful because of its concrete approach to preventing sexual abuse of children.

Lenett, Robin, and Dana Barthelme with Bob Crone. *Sometimes It's O.K. to Tell Secrets! A Parent/Child Manual for the Protection of Children.* New York: Tom Doherty Associates, 1986.
> Helpful for teachers as well as parents, this resource devotes five chapters to educating adults about the dangers and consequences of sexual abuse and about the importance of breaking the "barrier of silence" that surrounds abuse. Chapter 6 contains about 25 story situations which end with the question, What would you do?

Murphy, Elspeth. *Sometimes I Need to Be Hugged.* Weston, Ont./Elgin, Ill.: Cook, 1981.
> A paraphrase of Psalm 84 for children.

Sanford, Doris. *I Can't Talk About It.* Portland, Ore.: Multnomah Press, 1986.
> Annie, a child who is being sexually abused by her father, talks with God about her pain. Two noteworthy aspects are the book's sensitivity to abused children's tendency to blame themselves and its stress on the need for forgiveness. Not suitable to read in its entirety in the classroom, but the book may be helpful for approaching a child who has been abused.

Plummer, Carol A. *Preventing Sexual Abuse: Activities and Strategies for Those Working With Children and Adolescents.* Holmes Beach, Fl.: Learning Publications, 1984.
> Contains a skeleton outline of programs to prevent sexual abuse in K-6, 7-12, and programs for developmentally disabled persons. Other features are suggestions for setting up a prevention program, guidelines for instructors, and curriculum guides. A helpful teacher resource, but be aware that suggested roleplay situations require careful evaluation. Order from the publisher: P.O. Box 1326, Holmes Beach, Florida 33509.

Talking About Touching—Grades 1-3. Seattle: Committee for Children.
> This material is costly, but comprehensive. It uses photos to elicit classroom discussion and covers physical abuse and neglect as well as sexual abuse prevention. Included are 46 laminated lessons, teacher guide, and parent activity sheets. For more information or to obtain a catalog of other materials, contact Committee for Children, 172 - 20th Ave., Seattle, Washington 98122-5862; phone 800-634-4449.

What Every Kid Should Know About Sexual Abuse. South Deerfield, Mass.: Channing L. Bete, 1986.
> A coloring and activities booklet that covers basics of sexual abuse prevention. To order contact the publisher: 200 State Rd., South Deerfield, Massachusetts 01373-0200; phone 800-628-7733.

LESSON 1: SAFETY IN THE HOME

Preparation/materials
- Student Activities 1–5
- Symbols for hazardous substances or labels with warning signs and symbols
- Optional: contact local poison control center for stickers to label poisonous substances in the home.

Objectives
- Students will become aware of their responsibility to prevent accidents.
- Students will become aware of the potential safety hazards at home.
- Students will review the poison prevention rules.

Background
Accidents in and around the home are a major cause of disability and death for every age group. This level focuses on the variety of accidents that occur to children and adults at home. The major categories of home accidents are falls, fires, electrical accidents, and poisonings.

• •

Lesson

1. Discuss accidents. What they are and why do many of them happen? Ask: "What is an accident?" Discuss student answers. Make the point that we never plan to have an accident; accidents happen unexpectedly. Explain that we can make choices that help to prevent accidents from happening both to ourselves and to others.

2. Identify types of choices we make that can help to prevent accidents: keeping equipment in good working order (bike brakes, lights, electrical cords), storing dangerous things carefully (saws, razors, cleaning fluids), keeping walkways clear (no stuff to trip over on stairs, etc.), and paying attention to traffic rules. Write the list on the board.

3. Ask whether accidents take place at home. Have students look at activity pages 1–4. Give students plenty of time to examine the pictures and to point out what the potential dangers are. How can accidents be prevented in these areas? Review/stress these safety rules: don't drink, eat, or taste any unknown substances; don't use tools meant for adult use only. Review the symbols for poison and other hazardous materials. Display the symbols throughout this unit. Teach the following "alert" words: *warning, caution, danger, poison.* Identify places students may see these words.

4. **Student activity.** Student Activity 5 in the workbook is for students to take home and complete. Direct students to think of ways they can improve safety in each room. If you wish, have them fill in the names of rooms you wish them to check. If you have obtained stickers (Mr. Yuk or Officer Ugg) from a poison control center, distribute them so students can label potentially dangerous substances found in their homes.

Compare the completed check sheets. Do most homes have the same trouble spots?

5. **Closure:** "What are some choices we can make to prevent accidents both to ourselves and others? (Elicit responses.) Making a home safety check will help us and our families to avoid accidents at home."

• •

Related Activities

1. Center activity: practice reporting emergencies. Review the following steps: (1) call the local emergency number, usually 911 or 0 for Operator; (2) give your name; (3) tell where you are (should know home address); (4) tell what the emergency is; (5) stay on the phone until the other person hangs up or tells you to hang up. Write these steps on a card and put them at a center with a few telephones (both touch tone and dial types). Students can practice reporting emergencies. Consider recording their emergency "calls" and then listening to the tape.

2. If your area has a poison control center, request a representative to give a presentation.

3. Roleplay emergency situations at home (fire is covered later). Have one person report the accident.

LESSON 2: ON THE ROAD

Preparation/Materials
- Pictures of traffic signs
- Optional: chart paper
- Optional: use masking tape to mark off an "intersection" in the classroom.

Objectives
- Students will review pedestrian and car safety.
- Students will be introduced to bike safety.

Background
If students are very familiar with traffic and pedestrian safety rules, you may wish to begin with the Simon Says game (described in step 5) to review and to identify weak spots to reteach. However, if the class is unfamiliar with the rules, it may take more than one session to cover the material.

• •

Lesson

1. Show students the pictures of traffic signs and ask them to identify the meaning of each sign.

2. Review basic pedestrian rules with the class. Elicit the rules from the class and write them on the board or on a chart. Add any rules the students miss. Include the following:
    - Walk on the sidewalk or grass away from the curb. Watch out for cars backing up in driveways.
    - Cross the street at the corner. Stay in the crosswalk if there is one.
    - Look all ways for cars before crossing. Listen for approaching cars. Watch for turning cars (and bicycles).
    - If there is a traffic/crossing light, obey the light.
    - Walk rather run across the street.

    If you wish, mark off an "intersection" on the classroom floor and have students practice watching for cars and crossing the street.

3. Take the class on an imaginary car ride. Ask students to think about how they can be safe while they're riding. Then tell them to pretend they are riding in a car. Add sound effects of getting in a car, closing door, and starting the car to add interest. Ask: "What are ways to be safe in a car?" (Wear seat belts, sit quietly, don't distract the driver.) Have the class pretend to buckle up and stay buckled up until you say they have arrived at their destination.

4. Then have the class pretend to be riding bikes on a sidewalk. (Most second graders are most likely still staying close to home and riding on sidewalks. The situation may be different for students living in busy, urban areas or in rural or quiet suburban areas.

Adapt the material to fit your particular situation. Bicycle safety is taught in more detail in grade 3.) Again, add sound effects to simulate a bike ride. Ask: "What are ways to be safe while we're riding bikes on the sidewalk?" Include the following:

- Dress properly. Tie shoelaces and avoid clothes that can catch in the bike chain.
- Keep bikes in good repair.
- Watch what's going on around you; watch out for cars backing out of driveways.
- Keep both hands on the handlebars. Don't try to carry things.
- Walk the bike across streets and obey any traffic signs.
- Watch out for pedestrians on the sidewalk.
- Avoid loose gravel or broken cement.
- Wear bike helmets.

Finally, arrive back home and park the bike in an appropriate place.

5. Play a Simon Says game to review the safety rules. Call it a Safe Simon Says game. If Simon says a safety rule, have students pantomime the rule. But if Simon suggests unsafe behavior, have students put their hands up in a stop gesture or sit down.

6. **Closure.** Reflect on the lesson with questions such as the following:
   - "Which safety rule is the hardest for you to remember or to follow?"
   - "Why is knowing safety rules not enough?" (We need to choose to follow them.)
   - "How can following safety rules help us to love our neighbors as ourselves?"

• •

Related Activities

1. Contact the education department of the local police department and request a police officer to give a traffic safety presentation.

2. Review school playground rules. Have students walk around the playground and explain the reasons for the rules. Together identify any potential safety hazards on the playground.

3. Have groups of students make posters showing safety rules. Assign each group a specific area of safety.

LESSON 3: STRANGER EDUCATION

Preparation/Materials
- Health puppet
- Plan puppet script.

Objectives
- Students will review basic rules of stranger safety.
- Students will recognize specific situations that pose danger.
- Students will develop self-protection skills.

Background

For their safety, children need to learn basic rules regarding strangers. These rules periodically need to be repeated so that children are very familiar with them. Keep the discussion low key. Assure the class that most strangers are friendly and helpful and that it's not likely they'll be harmed by strangers. Compare stranger education to fire safety education: fire isn't very common, but being prepared to deal with a fire helps to keep us safe.

Make parents or other adult caregivers aware of the material covered in this lesson. Encourage them to reinforce the material and talk to their children about any special rules they have about strangers. What are family rules about telephone conversations with strangers and answering the door at home?

Lesson

1. Use one of the health puppets to get across the idea that when children are with the adults who care for them it's fine for them to chat with friendly strangers. Have Chris, for example, tell the class how much she has always enjoyed talking with people. Even when she was a little girl sitting in a stroller, she always greeted people—on the sidewalk, in the store, at the park, in the library. When she was older, she asked everyone she met questions: "What are you doing? What's your name? Where are you going? What's in your bag?" The strangers always—well, almost always—smiled at her questions and tried to answer them.

    Have Chris ask the students if they know anyone like that. Do they like talking to people they meet, too? Chris can comment that when they are with the adults who are taking care of them, it's fun to talk with and respond to friendly strangers. End the introduction by telling students that although most strangers are okay, once in a while there are bad strangers, so they should be careful about strangers.

    Alternative option: use the puppet script suggestion to create a story to tell the class.

2. Discuss stranger safety rules. Begin by identifying who strangers are. Stress that anyone they and their family don't know well is a stranger—even if it's someone they may recognize (for example, grocery store clerk or ice cream seller). Then elicit safety rules from the students. Write the rules on the board, adding any the children omit. Include the following points:

- Stay near family/adult caregiver in public places.
- Don't go anywhere with a stranger. Don't ever go for a walk or a ride with a stranger, even though he or she claims to know your parents or claims to want to give you a ride home.
- Don't approach a stranger's car, even if he or she wants to give you something or wants you to help with something.
- Don't take anything from a stranger—including something you'd really like to have such as a toy or candy.
- If strangers approach you with requests (as above), say no and run away. (Don't run away to hide; run toward other people).
- Tell other trusted adults or parents. (Identify specific people to tell.)

3. Talk over some What If? situations. Have volunteers act out some of the scenarios and discuss what they should do. Consider using the following situations:
   - You're walking home from school with a friend. It's raining and you're walking together under an umbrella. A woman in a shiny car drives up, rolls down the window, and offers to give you both a ride home. She says she knows your family. What should you do?
   - You're shopping at the mall with your older sister. She tells you to sit down on a bench and wait for her while she goes to get some ice cream cones. While you're waiting, a friendly man comes along and sits next to you. He says your sister wants you to meet her at the ice cream store. He'll show you where it is. Should you go with him?
   - You and your friend take the same bus home from school. Two times you've seen a woman sitting in a car across from the bus stop watching you when you get off the bus in the afternoon. What should you do?
   - You're with your family at a restaurant. The man at the next table hears you tell a joke and he laughs. He asks you if you know any more jokes. Should you talk to him?
   - You're sitting outside on the lawn playing a game with your friend. The mail carrier walks past whistling, carrying the mail for your house. He says, "Well, hello. I haven't seen you two together for a long time. What are you playing?" Should you talk to him?

4. **Closure.** Briefly summarize the lesson by reading the safety rules on the board. End on a positive note by reminding students that most strangers are okay and most children never come across a bad stranger. Remind them, too, that God has given them family members to take care of them and has provided people in the community (crossing guards, bus drivers, police officers, school staff members, neighborhood parents) to watch out for them.

Related Activities

- Reinforce lesson concepts by reading stranger education books. Here are a few title suggestions.

  Who Is a Stranger and What Should I Do? by Linda Walvoord Girard

  "Natalie's Story" in *Sometimes It's O.K. to Tell Secrets!* by Robin Lenett, and Dana Barthelme.

  Strangers by Dorothy Chlad

  Strangers Don't Look Like the Big Bad Wolf! by Janis Buschman and Debbie Hunley.

LESSON 4: LEARN NOT TO BURN

Preparation/Materials

- Use masking tape to outline a large sample home floor plan on classroom floor as illustrated:

Bedroom	Kitchen
Bedroom	Living Room

- Make a large copy of the Student Activity booklet on tagboard. Punch holes and use metal rings to form a large book.
- Masking tape
- Student Activity
- Optional: write a letter to parents (see step 5).

Objectives

- Students will review basic fire safety rules.
- Students will identify a home escape plan.

Background

This lesson is adapted from the National Fire Protection Agency's *Learn Not to Burn* curriculum. According to the agency, "more than 65 percent of fatal fires in homes occur between 8 P.M. and 8 A.M. Many of the victims are found in bedroom areas even though the fire was confined to another area of the dwelling." For this reason, planning escape routes from bedrooms is vital. The agency recommends making home escape plans and then practicing E.D.I.T.H. (Exit Drills In The Home) as important safety precautions.

Lesson

1. Ask students if they have a home escape plan in case of a fire in their home. Ask: "Do you practice your plan with your family? Why is it important to have a home escape plan?"

2. Use the floor plan to demonstrate a possible home escape plan. Stand in one of the rooms and tell students to pretend this is their house. Tell the students that when the smoke detector goes off or if they see smoke or a fire, they should hurry out of the house and go to the meeting place decided on earlier. (Walk through the house and out the door to the meeting place.) Explain that then you quickly count to make sure everyone was out of the house and then send one person next door to call the fire department. If someone is missing, tell the fire fighters and they will rescue him or her. Stress that they should never "hide" from a fire and that once out of the building they should never go back in—for any reason.

3. Assign students to work with family members to design and practice a home escape plan. Ask parents (a sample letter requesting help is included in step 5) to assist children by making drawings of their homes showing evacuation routes. You may want to ask students to take the drawings to school to share with the rest of the class.

4. Show the class the large *Learn Not to Burn* book and review/teach fire safety rules. Go over each picture and elicit the appropriate fire safety rule from class members. Reteach

rules and provide information as necessary. (Refer to the parent letter in step 5 for rules to go with each page.)

5. **Student activity.** Students will make mini fire safety booklets to help them review fire safety rules. They can color the pictures, Then assemble the booklets by (1) cutting on the dotted lines, (2) putting pages in proper order, (3) folding the pages in half and stapling the booklet in the center. (If you wish to have students make this at a center, make an audio recording of the instructions and place both the recording and activity materials at the center.)

"Walk" through the booklet with the class, asking class members to recall the rule or rules belonging with each picture. To encourage parents to conduct a similar review at home, compose a letter for students to take home with their booklets.

Sample letter to parents:

We are studying fire safety at school, and we would like you to help your child develop and practice a home escape plan. We ask that you draw a rough plan of your home, mark the escape routes, and walk through the routes with your child. Please consider alternate escape routes in case one room exit is blocked. Also, designate a meeting place outside the house so that family members can quickly gather and be accounted for.

Your child's Learn Not to Burn booklet pictures basic fire safety rules discussed at school. What rules does your child remember?

Page 2	Know your escape route. Never "hide" from a fire.
	To escape when smoke is heavy, crawl low along the floor.
	Use smoke alarms.
	Be sure your house number clearly shows.
Page 3	Children should not use candles, lighters, or matches.
Page 4	Use campfires safely. Douse fires completely.
	Don't get too close to campfires.
Page 5	Use a screen in front of a fireplace.
	Don't play with the fire.
Page 6	Beware of plugs and cords.
	Never put something (other than a plug) into an outlet.
Page 7	If your clothes ever catch on fire, don't run. Call for help, put your hands over your face, and stop, drop, and roll to smother the fire.
Page 8	Dial 911 (or your local emergency number) to report a fire. Children should be able to state their address.

6. **Closure.** Have students make "Today I learned (or relearned) … statements." Stress the importance of making safe choices.

Related Activities

1. Invite fire fighters to school to discuss fire safety issues. Ask them to focus on home evacuation.

2. Review and practice the crawling-low-in-smoke or the stop, drop, and roll techniques learned at grade levels K and 1.

3. Share the Learn Not to Burn Booklets with another class. Have students use the teacher visual of the book to make a presentation to kindergarten or grade 1 students.

LESSON 5: APPROPRIATE/INAPPROPRIATE TOUCH

Preparation/Materials
- Student Activities 1–3
- Visual of choice for teaching body private zone (Student Activity 2 or Teacher Visual)

Objectives
- Students will review the difference between appropriate and inappropriate touch.
- Students will generate ways to protect themselves in specific situations of risk.
- Students will identify sources of help.
- Students will recognize the difference between good and bad secrets.

Background

Some may question the need for child abuse education in Christian schools, but reliable research has shown that abuse does occur in Christian families and communities. And the rate of abuse is comparable to or only a little lower than that of the population as a whole. So although we may wish to believe that the problem does not exist in Christian communities, the facts do not support that view. Christian communities need to face the reality of abuse and help students develop skills for dealing with it.

Each level of the health education curriculum addresses the problem of sexual abuse. Since this is a sensitive subject, it is important for the school to contact parents or caregivers in advance and inform them of lesson content. You may wish to do this by letter or by meeting with parents. (Your school administrator may prefer to hold a meeting to which parents of all grades are invited. Some schools discuss the content of child abuse prevention lessons at a parent orientation meeting during the first week of school.) Good communication with the home will give parents the opportunity to work with the school and to reinforce safety concepts.

The central focus of this lesson is safety, not sex education. In this unit students have been learning about safety. Now they are learning about one more type of safety—safety from sexual assault. Students who are aware of the danger of sexual abuse and know to protect themselves are less likely to become victims of sexual abuse.

To be effective, sexual abuse prevention education needs to cover the following basic areas in age-appropriate ways: (1) recognizing sexual abuse or differentiating between appropriate and inappropriate touch, (2) learning self-protection skills and techniques, and (3) identifying sources of help. We want to emphasize that presenting information on the subject of sexual abuse is not sufficient. Students also need to develop skills—decision-making skills and self-assertive protection skills. They must not only understand what inappropriate touch is, but must also understand what they can do about inappropriate touch.

It's also vital to present the material in a nonthreatening way. Introduce the topic of touch in a way that makes you and the class feel comfortable. Having the classroom teacher present the material is preferable because an atmosphere of trust and rapport has already been established. If you are unable to teach the lesson comfortably, however, consider asking another qualified person to teach it, perhaps another teacher on the school staff. This is an important safety lesson, and it should be presented in a supportive environment.

As you teach the lesson, be clear and direct; use correct names when referring to body parts. If a child should begin to report abuse during class (an unlikely event), talk with him or her later and consult with school staff.

Lesson

1. Refer to Student Activity 1 showing various touches and use it to introduce the discussion of touches in a comfortable way. Identify the three ways to rate touches: good, bad, and confusing. Explain what confusing means. Then look at each picture and talk about what it shows. Have students rate each touch. (The squeeze and the piggy-back ride may be rated confusing.) Give students opportunity to identify other confusing touches such as tickling, love pats that are almost a shove, too-tight hugs.

2. Discuss inappropriate touching of private body parts. Use Student Activity 2 in the student workbook and include the following material in the discussion: God made all parts of the body good. Some parts are private. Our private parts are our genitals (vulva or penis) and buttocks (preferably use correct words for body parts, but if you prefer, identify private parts as the area covered by a bathing suit). Who may touch our private parts? Doctors, nurses, and other health professionals may touch private body parts for medical treatment. Parents may touch private parts when they are taking care of an injured area. Use the Teacher Visual if deemed appropriate to discuss inappropriate touching.

3. Ask: "What should you do if someone wants to touch your private parts or wants you to touch their private parts?" (Say no, go away, and tell a trusted adult.) Elicit from students people they could go to for help and write the list on the board (family members, teachers, friends, pastors). If one adult doesn't try to help them, they should ask someone else. Stress that sexual abuse is always the abuser's fault and never the child's fault.

4. Present some specific situations and have students talk about what they should do. Encourage them to give specific, realistic plans. Suggested situations:
   • "What if a stranger at a park comes from behind the bushes and shows you his private parts?"
   • "What if someone offers to give you something you really like if you'll take off your clothes?"
   • "What if someone suggests you play a special game together and keep the game a secret? Then they tell you to start the game by taking off your clothes."

5. Follow up on the last situation and differentiate between good and bad secrets. Ask students for examples of good secrets (surprise parties, Christmas or birthday presents). Ask: "How do good secrets make you feel?" Then talk about bad secrets. Explain that secrets are bad when they upset or frighten us. Give some examples of bad secrets. Include having someone touch them inappropriately and then telling them to keep it a secret.

6. **Student activity.** In Student Activity 3, students should write the three steps of self-protection in proper sequence in the talking balloons (say no, get away, tell someone).

They can refer to the word bank for help. Ask students to think of three people they could tell and then fill in the names in the space provided on the activity sheet (protect children's privacy by refraining from questioning them about the names).

7. **Closure.** Summarize the lesson and conclude by telling students that God wants us to touch each other in good ways and that good touches can show how much we love and care for each other.

8. **Unit review.** To review unit safety concepts play a final Safe Simon Says game. Consider having groups of students compare four or five statements to use in the game.

• •

Related Activities

1. Use resources such as the following to reinforce or expand the lesson:
   Sometimes It's O.K. to Tell Secrets! by Lenett and Barthelme contains brief read-aloud stories dealing with secrets. Each ends with the question; What would you do?
   Good Hugs and Bad Hugs: How Can You Tell? by Angela Carl
   My Body Is Private by Linda Walvoord Girard

   Private Zone by Frances S. Dayee
   It's Okay to Say No by Amy Bahr
   It's My Body by Lory Freeman

2. Make a bulletin board showing good touches. Students can cut out magazine pictures depicting good touches and mount them on construction paper.

Learning About Medicines and Drugs

Goals

- Students will recognize how choices about using medicines and drugs affect health and safety.
- Students will choose to take responsibility for making health choices.

Background

This unit continues to raise consciousness about health and safety issues and to promote awareness of the important health choices students make daily. The unit also introduces the topic of substance abuse and lays the foundation for lessons at higher levels. We are all aware that substance abuse is a serious problem in North American society, and *Horizons Health* addresses the problem at each grade level. At grade 2, students distinguish between prescription and over-the-counter medications and between medicines and drugs. They also learn about the effects of three of the most common drugs in our society—caffeine, nicotine, and alcohol.

AIDS—acquired immune deficiency syndrome—is not specifically addressed in kindergarten, grade 1, or grade 2. However, concepts essential to understanding AIDS are introduced. Students learn about communicable disease and about wellness behaviors to reduce risk of infection. Lessons in higher grades build on this information so that students receive AIDS education in developmentally appropriate ways.

Nonetheless, because AIDS receives wide attention in the media, even very young children may be aware of AIDS and raise questions about it. Teachers must be prepared to answer their questions with age-appropriate information. The United States Department of Health and Human Services' *Guidelines for Effective School Health Education to Prevent the Spread of Aids* (MMWR Supplement, January 29, 1988) suggests that education about AIDS for students in early elementary grades should center on allaying excessive fears and consist of these three concepts:

- AIDS is a disease that is causing some adults to get very sick, but it does not commonly affect children.
- AIDS is very hard to get. You cannot get it just by being near or touching someone who has it.
- Scientists all over the world are working hard to find a way to stop people from getting AIDS and to cure those who have it.

Vocabulary

Integrate the following suggested vocabulary:

germs	mouth	cough	smoking	over-the-counter
symptom	nicotine	sick	inhale	air sac (or alveoli)
prescription	bacteria	exhale	oxygen	bronchial tubes
drugs	tobacco	lungs	immunization	windpipe (or trachea)
caffeine	alcohol	smoke	virus	

Lesson Resources

Lesson 1

Berger, Melvin. *Germs Make Me Sick! A Let's-Read-and-Find-Out Book.* New York: Harper, 1985.
Berger explains how germs make us sick and identifies two kinds of germs—bacteria and viruses.

How to Catch a Cold. Filmstrip. Disney Educational Media. (Distributed in Canada by McIntyre Media.)

Lesson 2

Drugs, Poison, Little Children. Filmstrip/audiocassette. Educational Activities.
Reinforces the concept that sniffing, tasting, or ingesting any unknown substance can be deadly.

Skidmore, Steve. *Poison! Beware! Be an Expert Poison Spotter.* Brookfield, Conn.: Millbrook Press, 1991.
Detailed information about poison in the everyday environment.

Lessons 3-5

About Alcohol and Other Drugs: A Coloring and Activities Book. South Deerfield, Mass.: Channing L. Bete.
A 16-page booklet with puzzles, quizzes, and coloring. Order from the publisher: 200 State Road, South Deerfield, Massachusetts 01373-0200; phone 800-628-7733.

I Love Not Smoking: A Coloring Book for Non-Smoking Children. Vancouver, B.C.: Namchi, 1982.
A coloring book that creates a positive image of non-smokers. Each page gives an advantage of not smoking ("I can run faster, if I don't smoke"). Order from the publisher: P.O. Box 33852, Station D, Vancouver, British Columbia V6J 4L6.

Drugs and Alcohol: "Play It Straight." Circle Pines, Minn.: American Guidance Service.
A board game for grades 2 and up that focuses on "peer pressure, health facts, self-discipline, and communication." The players make decisions about situations.

Drugs Can Be Dangerous. Filmstrip/audiocassette. QED Products.
This filmstrip (seven-minute running time) teaches students about the danger of taking medications not prescribed to them and/or not given them by their parents.

Hawley, Richard, Robert Petersen, and Margaret Mason. *Building Drug-Free Schools. Part 2.* New York: American Council for Drug Education, 1986.
The Council's program consists of a four-part drug prevention kit—three written guides and a film. Part 2, a curriculum for grades K-12, contains essential drug information for teachers and gives the developmental basis for the schoolwide curriculum.

Lungs Are for Life-2. New York: American Lung Association.
Modules for grades K-4 include teacher guide, poster, and reproducible activity sheets. Grade 2 materials include lessons on air pollution/smoking. Available from local chapter or contact American Lung Association, 1740 Broadway, New York, New York 10019.

No Smoking Coloring and Activities Book. South Deerfield, Mass.: Channing L. Bete.
   Uses a game and puzzle approach to get across the no-smoking message. Order from the
   publisher: 200 State Road, South Deerfield, Massachusetts 01373-0200; phone 800-628-7733.

Safety Kids Play It Smart Stay Safe from Drugs. Washington, D.C.: Narcotics Education.
   A musical for grades 1-6. Includes 8 upbeat sing-along songs with acted-out situations to
   teach the dangers of alcohol and drugs. Can be performed as a program. Audiocassette,
   activity books available. Order from the Health Connection, Narcotics Education, Inc. 6830
   Laurel St. NW, Washington, D.C. 20012-9979.

Seixas, Judith. *Alcohol: What It Is, What It Does.* New York: Greenwillow, 1981.

_____. *Tobacco: What It Is, What It Does.* New York: Greenwillow, 1981.

_____. *Drugs: What They Are: What They Do.* New York: Morrow, 1991.

Starting Early: An Alcohol Education and Traffic Safety Program for Elementary School, K-6. Kit. 2nd
edition. Falls Church, Va.: American Automobile Association, 1982.
   Consists of lesson plans and activities and a video. Contact the local AAA branch for
   ordering information or write to AAA, Traffic Safety Department, Falls Church, Virginia
   22047.

Lesson 6

Chapman, Dorothy. *My Body Is Where I Live.* Circle Pines, Minn.: American Guidance Service,
1989.
   A full-color picture book and cassette tape providing information about taking care of the
   body, cleanliness, healthy food, exercise, and dangers of drugs. Intended for kindergarten
   through grade 4.

LESSON 1: GERMS MAKE ME SICK

Preparation/Materials
- Write the vocabulary listed in step 1 on the board or a chart.
- Student Activities 1a and 1b
- Student Activity 2
- Optional: health puppets

Objectives
- Students will review the role of germs in causing illness.
- Students will review ways to prevent germs from spreading.

Background
This lesson is basically a review lesson. In grade 1 students learned the difference between communicable and noncommunicable diseases and ways to prevent the spread of communicable disease. However, these basic health concepts need repeating periodically to raise student awareness of healthy behaviors and to encourage them to make healthy choices.

Lesson

1. Write on the board the words *germs* and *sick* or *sickness*. Ask students what the connection is between germs and being sick. Briefly review that germs cause sickness. If you wish to make a more comprehensive review, cover (elicit from students if possible) the following facts:

   - Germs are all around (in air, water, and food, and on everything we touch). We can't see them with our eyes alone. Not all germs are harmful.
   - Bacteria and viruses are two kinds of germs that can make us sick. Viruses are tinier than bacteria. Doctors can give us medicines that kill bacteria or stop them from growing, but as yet there are no medicines to kill viruses.
   - Our bodies keep out germs in many ways (tiny hairs in the nose catch germs; skin covers our bodies; wetness in the mouth and throat keeps germs from entering).
   - Even when germs do get in, our bodies have other ways of fighting. Fighters—white cells and antibodies—in our blood attack and kill many of the germs.
   - We can help to prevent germs from getting into our bodies.

   Alternate option. Act out a little scene with the health puppets to dramatize how we feel when we're ill. Suggested scene: Chris offers to buy two ice cream cones—one for herself and one for Alex. Alex says thanks but he doesn't feel like eating ice cream. As their conversation continues, Chris inquires about what's the matter and Alex says he doesn't feel like eating anything. He decides to go home and tell his parents how he feels. He says he doesn't know why he feels the way he does and heads for home.

   Discuss the puppets' conversation with the class. Have they ever felt like the puppet who didn't feel like eating anything? Give students opportunity to talk about signs of illness (fever, rash, throwing up, no appetite, aches and pains). Ask: "Why do we get sick? What happens?" Briefly review the role of germs in causing many kinds of sicknesses (colds, flu, chicken pox, measles).

2. **Student activity.** Use Student Activities 1a and 1b to review and discuss ways to prevent germs from spreading. Have the class study each picture. Is the person doing something healthy or unhealthy? If unhealthy, why? And what is the healthy behavior that will help prevent germs from spreading? Then state or have students state the appropriate health rule (positively, if possible) as if they are addressing the person in the picture. Have students write the rule on the lines provided.

> Picture 1: Washing your hands with soap and water. Soap and water can get rid of germs. Stress that students should wash hands frequently (after handling pets, after using the toilet, and before eating). (The message could be, "Great! Wash your hands often.")

> Picture 2: Use your own straw (or cup or spoon). It's great to share, but don't pass illness around when you share.

> Picture 3: Wash cuts right away. Cuts and scrapes should be washed clean. Sometimes an adult may also put medicine and a bandage on the cut or scrape.

> Picture 4: Cover your mouth and nose (when you cough or sneeze). Coughing and sneezing into the air spread germs through droplet infection.

> Picture 5: Don't put things in your mouth (such as erasers, crayons, markers). Putting things that have been handled in your mouth gives germs the chance to get into your body.

> Picture 6: Don't put your mouth on the drinking fountain. That's another way to pick up others' germs.

3. **Student activity.** Read the story starter in Student Activity 2 with the class and then have students finish the story. You may wish to have the class identify which health rules Zak is ignoring. What might happen next? (Lynn might get sick because of Zak; Zak might break other rules—stick objects in his mouth that might have germs on them, etc., and then get sick himself.)

Students can share their story endings. Consider having groups act out some of the stories.

4. **Closure.** Summarize and evaluate with the following questions:
   - "What makes us sick?"
   - "Can we see germs? Why not?"
   - "Do all germs make us sick?"
   - "What are two kinds of germs that do usually make us sick?"
   - "What are some ways our bodies keep out germs?"
   - "What are some ways we can keep germs from spreading?"

Related Activities

- Have students go through magazines and newspapers and cut out pictures of health professionals who help keep them well.

Groups can make collages to display in the room.

LESSON 2: USING MEDICINE SAFELY

Preparation/Materials
- Chart paper
- Prescription container with label
- Optional: samples of over-the-counter medications
- Optional: puppets for student activity

Objectives
- Students will identify reasons for using medicine.
- Students will describe prescription and over-the-counter medicines.
- Students will apply what they have learned to specific situations.

Background
This lesson differentiates between prescription medicine and over-the-counter medications. Students need to understand that some of the common substances in our homes such as cough syrup and aspirin are medicines and should be treated as such. The stress in the lesson should be on not taking any substance without asking the responsible adult.

• •

Lesson

1. Begin the lesson by stating that everyone gets sick sometime. Engage students in a conversation about how it feels to be sick. Note that sometimes we get better by getting lots of rest and drinking fluids, but there are times when we need medicine. Write the word *medicine* on the top of a chart.

2. How does medicine help us? Elicit answers to this question from the class. Sum up the discussion and write the main points on the chart. Include the following ways:
   - Medicine helps us feel better. It controls our symptoms.
        Example: taking medicine such as aspirin for a headache or cough syrup for a cough.
   - Medicine helps fight the sickness.
        Example: pills for curing sore throats; ointments for eye infections; drops for ears or nose.
   - Medicine helps prevent sickness.
        Example: immunizations to prevent measles and other illnesses. Immunizations are often shots, but sometimes they are in liquid form.

3. Differentiate between prescriptions and over-the-counter medicines. Stress that many medicines are ordered by a doctor for a specific person and should be used by the person only. The doctor writes a prescription that is taken to the store; there a person who knows about medicine (a pharmacist) fills the prescription. Show students the prescription drug. Ask: "What do you think the label tells us? (Read the label.) What do you think might happen if you took medicine made for another person?"

Explain that other medicines can be bought without a prescription—at supermarkets or drugstores. Ask students to identify some of these types of medicines (cough syrups, aspirin, nose drops). Write the term "over-the-counter medicine" (OTC) on the board and explain what it means. Show students samples of OTCs. Ask: "What do you think these labels say? (Read one or more labels.) What do you think might happen if you took too much?"

End the discussion by stressing that students should never take medicine (prescription or over-the-counter medicine) from anyone other than a designated adult caregiver—even if the medicine tastes good.

4. Have students act out situations related to using medicine safely. Divide students into groups and suggest or assign a situation to each group.

   Suggested situations:
   * Children are playing doctor at friend's house. The friend takes medicine from the bathroom medicine cabinet to use for the "game."
   * A group of children find a bottle of medicine on a bench in the park or at a mall. Several want to "try" it.
   * A child who has a stomachache decides to use a sister's medicine. The child knows the medicine was prescribed for stomachache, and now he or she also has a stomachache.
   * A younger brother or sister doesn't feel well and wants a sibling to give aspirin or other medicine to feel better.
   * Children playing together decide to take cough syrup or other medicine because it tastes like candy.
   * A mother gave her child medicine for a sore throat this morning. Now the child's throat is hurting again. He or she has to decide whether to take some more without asking.

   Make sure that the danger of each situation is clear. Guide groups to stress the best way to deal with each situation. If necessary, reenact the scene to show safe behavior.

   Alternate option: Write a class story about children who play (or are tempted to play) with medicine.

5. **Closure:** "Today we learned about one of God's good gifts. Why can we call medicine a good gift? How can we show God how much we appreciate this gift?"

Related Activities

1. Center idea: review lesson vocabulary by making sentence strips and a set of vocabulary flash cards. Students fill in the blank of each sentence with one of the flash cards. Add other vocabulary cards/sentences as the unit progresses.

2. Focus on how we can help people (family members and others) who are sick. Have the class or individuals choose an appropriate project.

LESSON 3: THREE COMMON DRUGS

Preparation/Materials

- Pictures of cigarettes, beer, wine, liquor, coffee, tea, and cola drinks
- Student Activities 1 and 2
- Balloon to demonstrate inhaling and exhaling, one red and one blue for each student
- Optional: prepare a poster showing pictures of common drugs or make facsimiles of what drugs may look like (cooking herbs to represent marijuana, plastic bags of sugar and of flour to represent cocaine and heroin).
- Optional: make a large drawing of the student activity diagram on tagboard.

Objectives

- Students will be able to differentiate between medicines and drugs.
- Students will identify nicotine and alcohol as drugs.
- Students will be able to describe how nicotine enters and affects the body.

Background

Children of this age are often confused about the differences between a drug and a medicine. To make the distinction clear, at the primary level *Horizons Health* defines *medicine* as a substance used specifically to treat a symptom and to cure or to prevent a disease and defines *drug* as a substance that chemically alters the state or condition of the body and/or mind.

Why begin drug education at such a young age? One purpose is to protect children by preparing them learn to deal with situations that are all too common in our society. Another purpose is to help students form correct attitudes toward drugs from the beginning.

Certain drugs such as caffeine, nicotine, and alcohol are used so frequently and with such acceptance in our society that individuals who have not been taught otherwise fail to see that they can be damaging to health. The use (which can lead to abuse) of these drugs is promoted in the print and visual media and in television shows and films. It is very difficult for classroom teachers and health professionals to counter the strong message being portrayed by popular role models such as professional athletes and well-known actors. Education about substances needs to start young, before students are in situations where they are pressured to start using these drugs.

Let's consider the effects of these three common drugs. The first, caffeine, is found in foods and drinks (chocolate, cola drinks, coffee, cocoa, tea). Caffeine is a mild stimulant that increases the heart rate, causing the heart to work harder. Caffeine should be limited in a child's diet. Milk, water, and fruit juices are better choices for children than colas; fruits are sweet but healthful substitutes for chocolate.

The second, nicotine, is a stronger stimulant than caffeine. Found in tobacco smoke, it not only makes the heart work harder, but it also damages lung tissue. People breathing "second-hand" tobacco smoke may be harmed more than the smoker because sidestream smoke is unfiltered and contains more harmful products. (The tar in cigarette tobacco is also a health threat, but this lesson focuses on the drug nicotine.) Nicotine is extremely addictive.

The third drug, alcohol, is a depressant. It slows down the heart rate, causing sluggishness or drowsiness. It affects physical behavior and mood. The next lesson focuses on the effects of alcohol.

For steps 5-8 of this lesson we are indebted to *Lungs Are for Life-2* of the American Lung Association.

Lesson (2 days)

1. Open the lesson by differentiating drugs from medicine. Tell students that medicines are taken by sick people to help them become healthy, but drugs are taken by some people who are well to affect the way they feel or act. Explain that drugs can be swallowed, sniffed, smoked, or injected.

2. Since most students will be familiar with the concept of taking drugs from watching TV or from listening to the conversations of an older sibling or of adults, elicit from the class names of a few common drugs. If you have facsimiles or a poster, show these to the class. Explain that people use these drugs because they make them feel good for a short while, but these drugs are dangerous and can make them very sick and threaten life. Give students opportunity to ask questions; clear up any misconceptions they may have. Make clear that using these drugs are against the law for both adults and children.

3. Show students the pictures of cigarettes, beer, wine, liquor, cola, coffee, and tea and ask them to identify which contain a drug. Tell students that these are all items we see pictures of everyday and many people use these items every day, but these things do contain drugs. These are not against the law for adults to use, but most of them are against the law for children to use. Elicit from the class which items are against the law for children.

   Next, identify the drugs found in the pictured items:
   - caffeine—found in tea, coffee, chocolate, and cola. (Makes the heart beat faster and keeps people awake.) What are things students can eat or drink that don't have caffeine in them?
   - nicotine—found in the tobacco in cigarettes and pipe tobacco. (Nicotine enters the body through the smoke people breathe in.)
   - alcohol—found in beer, wine, and liquor. (Alcohol affects how the body works—how we talk and act.)

4. Teach lesson vocabulary: *drugs, caffeine, tobacco, smoke, nicotine, and alcohol.* Explain that in the rest of the lesson the class will find out about the effects of smoking on the body, and the next lesson will deal with the effects of alcohol.

5. Introduce Student Activity 1 illustrating how lungs work. Have the class label the different parts, filling in the blanks as you explain the diagram. Use an enlarged diagram or poster of the worksheet as a teaching visual. Have students use a red crayon to trace the movement of air from the air puff to the alveoli.

   Use an explanation similar to the following:
   - Air we breathe enters the lungs through the nose or mouth. (Ask students try breathing through mouth and then through nose; have them write the words *nose*

on line 1 and *mouth* on line 2.) Point out that when there is smoke in the air, or when someone is smoking, smoke enters the body through the nose or mouth.

- Next the air goes down the windpipe or trachea. (Have the class write *windpipe* or *trachea* on line 3.)
- Then air goes through the bronchial tube. (Direct the class to write *bronchial tubes* on line 4.) Point out how the tubes branch off so air can pass into the lungs. (Label the *lungs* on line 5.)
- Finally, the air goes into tiny air sacs or balloons in the lungs called alveoli. (Have the class write *air sacs* or *alveoli* on line 6.). Explain that from the alveoli a gas that we need which is in the air (oxygen) moves into the blood.

Then have students use a crayon of an other color to trace the path of "used up" air or carbon dioxide carried back to the lungs by the blood that is being exhaled.

6. Use a balloon to demonstrate the process of inhalation and exhalation. Teach the words *inhale* and *exhale*. Direct students to inhale and to exhale. Have them put their hands on their chests to feel the lung action.

7. Talk about the effects of smoking. Do students know about smoke-free areas? Why do they think people want these areas? Explain what effect smoking has on the body. Include the following information:
   - When smokers breathe out, not all of the smoke leaves the air sacs. Nicotine and other things in the smoke make the air sacs dirty. Smoking over a long period of time damages the lungs.
   - In order to take in enough fresh air, smokers have to breathe harder than nonsmokers.
   - Nicotine makes the heart beat faster.

8. **Student activity.** Introduce Student Activity 2. Discuss smoking as a habit. Tie into the discussion in Unit 5 about habits. Ask: "Why is it hard for some people to stop smoking even though they know it's not good for them?" (Nicotine is addictive; some habits are hard to break.) Stress that since smoking is not healthy, it's better not to start smoking.

Direct students to complete the rebus. Rebus solution: Smoking harms you. It makes your heart beat faster. Smoking is also bad for your lungs. Be smart. Don't smoke!

Have students complete the word search.

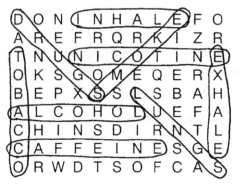

9. **Closure.** Summarize and evaluate with questions such as the following:
   - "Why do people take drugs?"
   - "What three drugs do we see or see pictures of almost everyday?"
   - "What foods is caffeine found in? What foods could you eat instead of those with caffeine?"
   - "What happens when a person smokes?"
   - "How does smoking harm us?"
   - "Why is it better not to start smoking?"
   - "What kind of drinks is alcohol found in?"

   End the lesson by telling students they will be learning more about the drug alcohol in the next lesson.

● ●

Related Activities

1. Research and discuss environmental pollution and its effects on the lungs.

2. Have students interview former smokers to find out why they quit smoking. Discuss the results of the interviews.

3. Make non-smoking posters. Write some messages on the board for students to use on their posters. (Thanks for Not Smoking! Be Smart/Don't Smoke!)

LESSON 4: EFFECTS OF ALCOHOL

Preparation/Materials
- Pictures of beer, wine, and liquor (from previous lesson)
- Student Activity

Objective
- Students will be able to describe the effects of alcohol on behavior.

Background
Responsible Christians vary in their attitudes toward the use of alcohol. Some feel that because of the potential for misuse and alcoholism, Christians should abstain from using alcohol. Others feel that adult Christians have the freedom to use alcohol, provided it is used in moderation and in a manner that does not lead others into misuse. Teachers will have to use their discretion in teaching this lesson.

• •

Lesson

1. Briefly review previous lesson concepts. Show students pictures of alcoholic beverages. Explain that these are against the law for children to use and that even small amounts of them are bad for children's growing bodies.

2. Discuss how alcohol affects the body. Explain that alcohol has the opposite effect of nicotine on the body. Alcohol makes the heart beat slower. In fact, it slows down the body in many ways—people think more slowly and breathe more slowly. If people drink too much alcohol, it will affect how they talk and walk. It also will keep them from seeing things clearly. When people can't control their bodies, we say they are "drunk." Conclude that although some adults may drink moderate amounts with dinner or when they're visiting with friends, it's never safe to drink too much. (You may also wish to introduce the idea of a designated driver.)

   You may wish to explain how alcohol can affect so many parts of the body. Tell students that when we drink alcohol, it first goes to the stomach. From there it goes on to the intestines, and from the intestines alcohol enters the blood. The blood carries alcohol to all parts of the body. Alcohol reaches the brain, too. Because the brain controls the body's actions, alcohol affects the way the whole body works.

3. **Student activity.** Turn to the worksheet and identify specific ways alcohol can affect a person's physical reactions. Discuss the picture, then have students write in the space provided the effects of alcohol. If necessary, write the answers on the board for students.

   Discussion ideas:
   - What accidents could alcohol cause? Have the class name as many as possible. (Tripping, stumbling, falling, getting burned, getting hurt using tools, or driving cars, motorcycles, or other machines.)

- If people drink and then drive, what specific problems might they have? (Not being able to stay on the road or driving over the center line, not being able to stop quickly, not being able to think quickly enough in an emergency.)
- Alcohol affects balance. People who have been drinking can't walk in a straight line, etc.
- People who drink too much alcohol frequently fall asleep or fall unconscious. They may not remember after they wake up what they said or did.

4. **Closure.** Briefly summarize the main ideas of the worksheet. If time permits, ask students to write on the back of the worksheet something they learned or relearned about alcohol from this lesson. Have volunteers share their statements with the rest of the class. Conclude by stating that alcohol can affect the way a person decides and acts.

LESSON 5: REVIEW OF SUBSTANCE USE/ABUSE

Preparation/Materials

- Student Activity—game cards and teacher statements (reproduced from the Teacher's Guide.) Create additional cards and statements if your class has more than 26 students or if you wish to review additional unit material.

Objective

- Students will review substance use/abuse concepts.

Lesson

1. Review material on substance use and abuse by playing the game Get That Word! Follow these steps:

    - First, teach or review the words on the game cards. Tell students they'll have to know these words to play the game. Discuss any words the students do not understand.

    - Second, divide the class into two teams. Have the students sit in a circle. The teacher should sit in the middle. Distribute the word cards, one to each student. Each team should have a set of the word cards. (One student on each team needs a word card to correctly complete each sentence the teacher will read.) As you pass out the cards, students should read their words silently. Make sure students know their words.

    - Explain how to play the game. The teacher reads one of the incomplete statements. The student on each team who has the correct word brings the card up to the teacher. The first person to bring the correct word wins a point. If the students don't understand the statement, reword it or give additional clues.

    Play the game until all the statements have been used. The team with the highest score wins.

2. **Closure.** Conclude by stressing that what the class has learned about drugs and their effects can help them to make safe and healthy choices as they grow up. If you wish, have students brainstorm a list of fun things to do that wouldn't require drugs.

LESSON 6: CULMINATING LESSON

Preparation/Materials

- Health puppets
- For student activity:
  Student Activity
  Construction paper, one sheet per student
  Optional: string as needed

Objectives

- Students will review behaviors that help them stay healthy.
- Students will praise and thank God for creating their amazing bodies.

• •

Lesson

1. Have Alex and Chris put on a final act.

    Script starter:
    > Chris: I feel sad, Alex. Because this is the last time we'll see these boys and girls.
    > Alex: C'mon, Chris. Don't be sad. We had great times.
    > Chris: That's true. You're right. Thanks for making me feel better. Besides, you know I think we learned some important things this year together. And that really makes me feel good.
    > Alex: What do you think was one of the most important things we learned?
    > Chris: I think it was learning that I could choose everyday to do things that help me be healthy and safe. It's not just up to my Mom or Dad or teacher or grandmother or grandfather, or … It's up to me. I can make healthy choices.
    > Alex: Good thinking Let's ask the class what they think was an important thing they learned in health.

    Alternative option: begin with a role reversal activity. Ask students to pretend to be a parent or health teacher. What would they tell or teach their children or students about health? What habits would they want to encourage (about bedtime, mealtime, use of TV, cleanliness, etc.)? Why?

    Then have one or both of the puppets engage the class in a conversation about health, using questions such as
    - "Why is it important for you to take care of your body?"
    - "What is one thing you do each day that helps keep you healthy?"
    - "Name one way you can help others be healthy."

    End with a good-bye from the puppets and a wish that students will keep making healthy choices.

2. **Student activity.** Turn to the activity sheet. Have students read the "habit balloons" and choose which are good habits. Direct them to color and cut out the good habit balloons. Have them paste the balloons on a piece of colored construction paper. Students

can glue strings or drawstrings from each balloon. Consider having students write a sentence or two to go with the picture.

3. **Closure.** Thank God for making our bodies in such a complex and wonderful way. Sing songs of praise and thanks to God. Have students identify specific things they have learned about in health to thank God for (for example, families, making us unique, giving us eyes to see with and ears to hear with). Talk about ways class members can show their thankfulness to God.

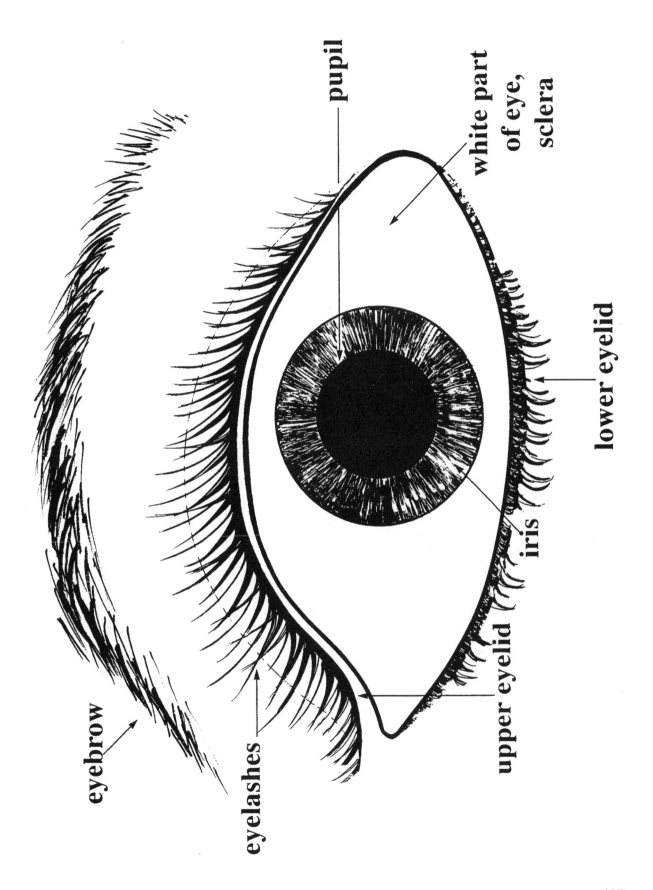

pupil

white part
of eye,
sclera

lower eyelid

iris

upper eyelid

eyelashes

eyebrow

Use this pattern to make your own hand puppet.

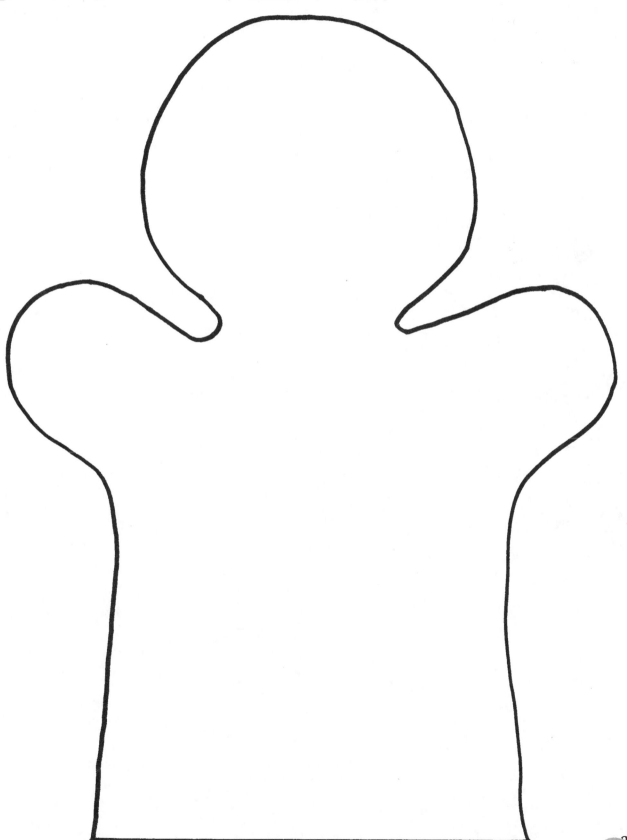

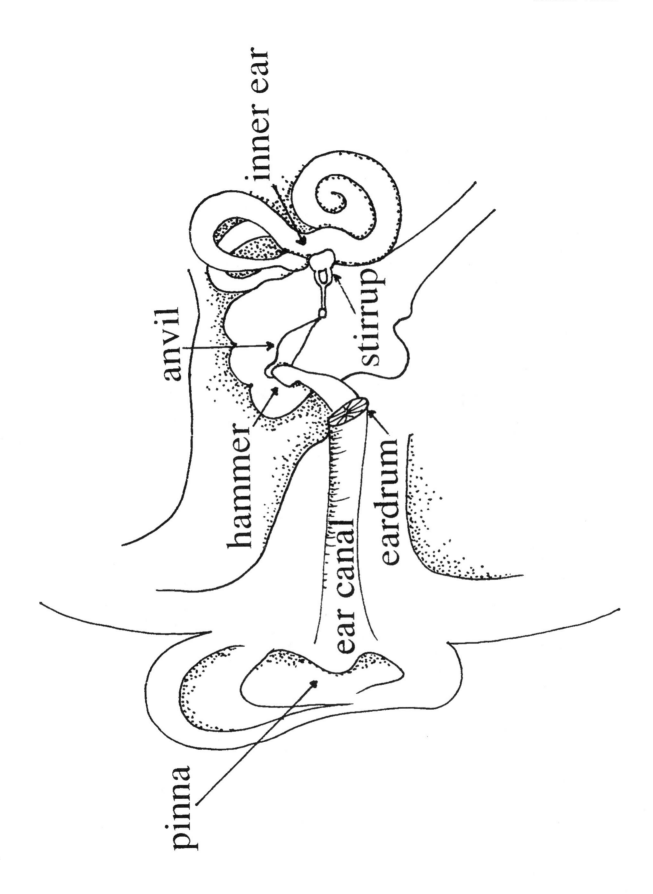

1. Nicotine is a (drug).

2. Nicotine is found in (tobacco).

3. Smoking harms your (lungs).

4. Nicotine and caffeine make your heart beat (faster).

5. Alcohol makes your heart beat (slower).

6. The drug found in beer, wine, and whiskey is (alcohol).

7. Cola and coffee both contain (caffeine).

8. Alcohol slows down the action of the (brain).

9. It's unsafe to drink alcohol and then (drive).

10. Too much alcohol can cause (accidents).

11. Caffeine is found in chocolate and (tea).

12. When people drink alcohol, they have less (control).

13. Alcohol affects a person's (balance).

drugs	brain	drugs	brain
tobacco	drive	tobacco	drive
lungs	accidents	lungs	accidents
faster	tea	faster	tea
slower	control	slower	control
alcohol	balance	alcohol	balance
caffeine		caffeine	

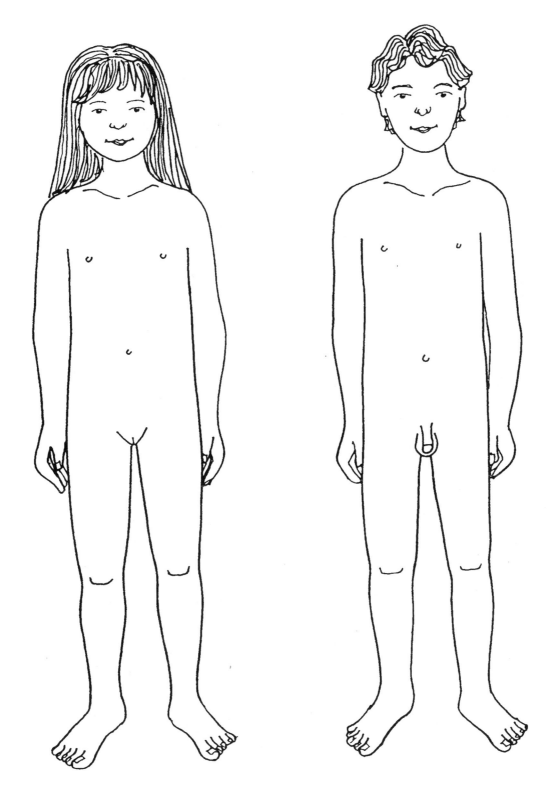

Permission granted to reproduce this page only.